WHERE

Lorna had fallen in love with Crete at
first sight, but her love for Jason
Peritakis took longer to develop. And
even when they both confessed their
love she was still racked by doubts.
Could she, an independent woman, ever
really be at home in Crete, with its very
different culture?

WHERE THE GODS DWELL

BY
CELIA SCOTT

MILLS & BOON LIMITED
15–16 BROOK'S MEWS
LONDON W1A 1DR

First published in Great Britain 1985
by Mills & Boon Limited

© Celia Scott 1985

Australian copyright 1985
Philippine copyright 1985
This edition 1985

ISBN 0 263 75120 1

Set in Monophoto Times 10 on 10½ pt.
01–0885 – 59348

Made and printed in Great Britain by
Richard Clay (The Chaucer Press) Ltd,
Bungay, Suffolk

There is a land called Crete in the middle of the wine-blue water, a handsome country and fertile, seagirt . . .

(The Odyssey of Homer, Book 19: Line 170)

CHAPTER ONE

THE timer went off with a noise like an angry wasp. Lorna lifted out the first print from the fixer tray and rinsed it carefully, using a length of borrowed hosepipe. She was using resin-coated paper for all her Greek photographs, so the rinsing didn't take long. Once she'd sponged away most of the water she examined the picture carefully. Her well-defined lips curved in a smile of satisfaction. It was great! Every detail of the shards that had been found on the 'dig' yesterday showed clearly. The distinctive Minoan design on the two larger fragments was particularly sharp. She placed the photograph on a fibre glass screen to dry and attended to the remaining prints.

A strand of silver-blonde hair slipped out of its hairband and stuck to her hot cheek. She tucked it behind her ear, thanking providence that she'd had the foresight to have it cut and styled at a fashionable Toronto salon before coming to Crete. Waist-length tresses might be okay for Canada, but for an archaeological photographer working under gruelling conditions, such abundance was nothing but a hot nuisance. And she liked the sense of freedom her new hairstyle gave her. Short on her neck, but dipping in sleek wings on either side of her face.

She put the last print on the screen to dry and let herself out of the stuffy little dark-room she'd fixed up in the taverna.

Her room-mate joined her on the way to the bedroom they shared. Susan was in her bathrobe and slippers, a sponge-bag in her hand, a damp towel on her shoulder.

'Did you leave me some water, Susie?' Lorna

enquired, opening the door to the bedroom and moving to the dresser for her shampoo.

'Never fear! There's lots of water tonight. Vasily filled the tank this morning.'

'Thank God for that!' Lorna said fervently, remembering the time their landlord had forgotten to fill the roof-top tank with water from the river. It had been a very grimy bunch of fieldworkers who had sat down to dinner that night.

She pulled her damp T-shirt away from her breasts. 'Lord! I'm hot,' she said, looking down at her dust-streaked denim skirt and dirty plimsolls, 'and filthy too. I must have half Crete's earth plastered all over me.' She peeled off her sweat-soaked clothes and wrapped herself in a cotton kimono that was the same shade of delphinium blue as her eyes.

'Oh! How I envy your figure, Lorna,' Susan said. She had laid down on her own bed, one plump leg poking out of her bathrobe, 'What are you? A size twelve?'

'I'm a ten,' Lorna admitted.

Susan sighed. 'It's not fair. I never lose weight.' Then her round face brightened. 'Maybe it's puppy-fat.'

'Puppy-fat! At twenty-six! Give me a break, Susie,' Lorna chuckled as she gathered up her towel and headed for the primitive shower. Still grinning she reflected that it was sometimes hard to believe that Susan was one year her senior. There were times when her chubby colleague acted more like a teenager.

Standing under the shower-head—that looked like the rose of an enormous watering-can that had been let into the ceiling—she cranked the handle to release a flow of sun-warmed water. She could feel the day's fatigue sliding away with the grime. While she vigorously shampooed her hair she sang, her voice echoing satisfyingly in the narrow stone-walled bathroom—'It's love's illusions I recall ... I ree ... eely don't know love at all,' she warbled happily as the water slid deliciously over her firm young body.

Winding her towel round her head and tying her kimono tightly round her slim waist she padded back to the bedroom to find Susan squeezing her ample bottom into a pair of peach-coloured polyester slacks. She struggled with the zipper, then gazed doubtfully at her reflection in the mirror.

'I think these pants must have shrunk,' she murmured.

Lorna diplomatically refrained from making any comment. She put on a pair of briefs and a lacy bra, then started riffling through her clothes that hung in the shared wardrobe. 'Aren't you going to be rather hot in slacks, Susie?' she asked. 'It doesn't get much cooler in the evenings, now that it's "flaming June".'

'I don't have anything else that's clean,' Susan said, looking gloomily at her peach-clad legs.

Lorna pulled a navy-and-white cotton tent dress out of the wardrobe and held it out to the other girl. 'Would you like to wear this? It should fit you, and it'll be a lot cooler than trousers.'

Susan looked at the attractive dress longingly. 'Could I, Lorna? That'd be terrific!' She divested herself of the tight-fitting trousers and Lorna helped her pull the tent dress over her head. The full material settled round Susan's roly-poly body, concealing her bulges, and making her appear inches taller. She turned slowly in front of the mirror and broke into a smile. 'It's great . . . gee! Thanks.'

'It does look good on you,' Lorna agreed, buttoning on a cream blouse and stepping into a full cherry-red cotton skirt, 'why don't you keep it, Susie,' she grinned, 'consider it an un-birthday present.'

Susan smoothed the crisp material. 'Lorna, are you *sure*? I . . . I love it . . . but . . .'

'It looks better on you than it does on me. Besides, I've got lots of clothes,' Lorna replied as she tied a soft black leather sash round her waist, 'one of the perks of doing fashion photography . . . I got things at cost.'

'Working in the fashion world must have been so glamorous. Don't you miss it?' Susan asked.

'Not a bit. It was fun at first, but after four years I was bored to death.'

'Wait till you've spent a few months grubbing around on this dig,' Susan said, 'you won't just be bored ... you'll be exhausted.' She pushed her stubby fingers through her short curls till they stood on end in a dark halo.

'Exhausted maybe, but never bored,' Lorna replied reflectively, 'digging up history is too exciting.'

'You certainly seem to be obsessed,' the older girl observed, watching Lorna apply mascara to her long curling lashes, 'I've noticed that fanatical look you get when we make an interesting find.'

'That's not a fanatical look, honey,' Lorna grinned, putting down her mascara and touching the high cheekbones of her oval face with a hint of blusher, 'that's my professional photographer's gleam.'

But she knew what Susan meant. Ever since she'd stepped off the plane at Iraklion three weeks before she'd felt as if she was under a magic spell. In some mysterious way it was as if Crete had claimed her for its own, binding her in a web of its ancient past and colourful present. Everything she saw, felt, and heard, found an echo in her heart, and she was enchanted.

She screwed silver hoop earrings into her ears and slipped two narrow matching silver bracelets on her fine-boned wrists. 'I don't know about you, Susie,' she said, 'but I'm hungry. It's been a long time since lunch.'

Her friend nodded enthusiastically. 'Me too. I could eat a horse.'

'You might have to settle for a goat, we're in Crete remember? Horses don't figure much on the menu here,' Lorna laughed, as the two girls, one tall and golden, the other short and brunette, made their way downstairs to dinner.

Outside, their colleagues were seated at a long table

under a plane tree. Vasily had strung small lights haphazardly around a shaky wooden frame, and they twinkled on to the shallow river that tumbled down to the valley below. The warm night air smelled of thyme and verbena.

'Lorna, where have you been? We have been thinking you were lost,' called Nikos Peritakis. He was one of the locals, and was helping on the dig. 'See! I have saved you a chair. Ela! Come!' he indicated a place next to him.

'There are two of us,' Lorna replied crisply. She disliked the way Nikos continually snubbed poor Susan, making it quite clear that he considered her too plain even for courtesy.

An extra chair was brought and Susan squeezed herself in on Nikos's other side. One of the American students poured Lorna a glass of retsina from the frosty communal jug. She sipped the icy resinous wine with pleasure, and helped herself to some crusty homemade bread and a spoonful of 'tzatziki'—a creamy cucumber and yoghurt dish flavoured with garlic.

'Have you heard the news?' Nikos asked, leaning close to Lorna's sleek blonde head. 'My family has returned from Athens.'

Lorna remained non-committal. Nikos was a cousin of the Peritakis family who owned, not only the land where the excavation was taking place, but also acres of olive, lemon, and orange groves, and also a large family villa higher up the mountain, plus vast tracts of land all over Crete. According to Nikos, his older cousin had tricked him out of his fair share of the inheritance when his uncle died, and now he was forced to augment his small income as best he could. He was very bitter about this, and although Lorna had a natural sympathy for any underdog, particularly one who had to put up with a tyrannical relative such as Jason Peritakis, Nikos's whining got on her nerves.

'The wedding arrangements for my youngest cousin

are completed,' Nikos told her. 'You can be sure her brother has seen to it that he has gained from the alliance. Jason would do nothing that was not for his benefit.' He swallowed his retsina and poured himself a fresh glass. 'It is sad to be poor, Lorna,' he went on mournfully, 'particularly when destiny intended that it should be otherwise. To be forced to work for one's livelihood.' His black eyes regarded her soulfully.

She broke off a piece of bread. 'I wouldn't know about that. I've always earned my own living,' she said shortly.

'Ah! But you make a lot of money, Lorna,' he waved his hand dismissively, 'and you are North American! With loving relatives who would not see you poor.'

Lorna was beginning to feel annoyed by this conversation. It was not the first time Nikos had implied that she came from a wealthy family. However, she had no intention of satisfying his curiosity. It was none of his business that her parents had died when she was a teenager, and that her older brother worked in Singapore. Nor that her older sister was married to a struggling country doctor in a remote area of British Columbia.

Mercifully, at this moment Vasily arrived with platters of food and the conversation languished.

At this country taverna there was no such thing as a menu. You were served what Vasily and his wife could get that day. It was simple, and always delicious. Tonight they ate 'youvarlakia' which turned out to be meat balls in lemon sauce, accompanied by a huge dish of home fried potatoes sprinkled with oregano, green beans stewed with tomatoes and mint, and bowls of Greek salad laden with salty feta cheese and local olives. A dish of oranges from the Peritakis's orange grove completed the meal.

By the time their coffee had been drunk the full moon had risen and on a whim Lorna decided to take a solitary walk before turning in. She said her good nights before Nikos, or anyone else, could offer to accompany her, and left the brightly lit garden.

Before she reached the road in front of the taverna her landlord called to her.

'Miss Lorna! Please. May I be speaking with you?' She turned back and joined him in the entrance hall. 'It is about your room of darkness.' Vasily spoke rather curious English. 'You are hearing that many more students come from Athens for helping with the diggings?'

She nodded. 'Mmm. Professor Spanakis said twelve are coming from the American School of Archaeology later this week.'

'And I am in the extremes,' Vasily confided, 'where to sleep these students?'

'And you need my dark-room,' she said.

'Your room of darkness would house four,' he admitted, 'perhaps with pressings five, but there is also the question of my refrigeration.' Lorna had been storing her film in the taverna's refrigerator. 'It is my experience that students have the appetites. I must be keeping more food ...' His good-natured face was creased with anxiety.

'No problem,' Lorna reassured him, 'I'll talk to Professor Spanakis tomorrow. We'll figure something out. Don't worry.'

She left the greatly relieved Vasily and started walking on the road that wound up the mountain. She wasn't sure how the problem was to be resolved, but something would have to be done. In any case she'd been getting progressively worried about the temperature in her makeshift dark-room ever since the weather had started to get hot. She might have to settle for polaroid shots only. But she didn't want to do that if it could be avoided. Besides, she still had to store the film somewhere cool. Well! She and the director of archaeology would have to sort it out tomorrow.

She reached the fork in the road where the path ran

down to the Minoan site. Tonight she ignored it and continued climbing the narrow mountain road. A gentle breeze pushed her skirt against her bare thighs and ruffled her smooth cap of hair.

She climbed steadily for about fifteen minutes, then stood at a bend in the road to catch her breath and admire the moonlit view.

Above her the dark presence of the mountain loomed. Olive trees huddled in the shadowed slopes below. Lorna made a mental note to return to this spot with her camera during the day and take some shots to add to her Cretan portfolio. She wanted to take enough pictures to make a book about the island. A good book that would say something honest about the place and its people.

She closed her eyes to savour the peace. She could hear a faint murmur from the river whose source was high in the peaks above. In the soft air she could imagine it sounded like music throbbing through the night ... it *was* music! She opened her eyes and followed the sound round the sharp bend and further up the road. Then she saw a square white building, like a dirty sugar cube, leaning against the base of the mountain. Its small windows were ablaze with light, and the sound of Greek music poured out of its half-opened door. From time to time she could swear she heard the sound of breaking crockery.

She peered through one of the grimy windows. The place was packed with people sitting on little cane-bottomed chairs which were grouped around tables. There was a small bar at the far end of the room. Near it, three men sat on a raised dais. One played a small Cretan fiddle, one a guitar, and the third was playing the penetrating three-stringed Cretan lyre. In a cleared space in front of the musicians, men, their arms on each other's shoulders, danced. Now and then one of the dancers would pick up a china plate from one of the tables and smash it to the ground, then continue to dance among the fragments.

Unobtrusively Lorna edged her way into the smoky atmosphere and seated herself at a small table near the bar. When the dance came to an end there was no applause, for it had not been a public display, but a private expression of the dancers' emotions. The musicians took a quick swallow of beer, then started to play again. This time their music was muted.

Lorna ordered a lemonade from the stocky barman. Unlike every other Cretan she had met so far he seemed dour and unsmiling. He ignored her *efharisto*—thank you—and when he set the bottle and glass before her his lips were tight with disapproval.

She looked round the smoky room. As her eyes grew used to the gloom she began to take note of the bar's occupants. There were some young men in uniform, no doubt on leave from the naval base at Souda Bay, some older men, and a few shepherds wearing the native Cretan dress of baggy trousers tucked into high boots, a cummerbund wound round the waist, and a black turban tied over the head so that the knotted fringe fell over the forehead.

Then she realised that she was the only woman in the place! That explained the barman's surly manner. She had entered a male stronghold. And while no Cretan would ever be inhospitable to a stranger he had made it clear she was not welcome. Well, she would leave as soon as she'd drunk her lemonade. Till then she intended to listen to the music, tactfully watch the various characters around her, and generally soak up the atmosphere.

The music grew louder now, pulsing and soaring. Beating against the smoke-grimed walls like the wings of an eagle. Lorna saw the figure of a man detach itself from a shadowy group near the door and go to the cleared space. He stood for a moment in the centre of the dancing area, his arms raised sideways, the light from the hanging oil lamp falling on his dark wavy hair and sunburnt face. Then he turned to face her and started to dance.

He was much taller than any of the other men in the room, with powerful shoulders and a strong neck. When he swayed to the plangent rhythms she was aware of his flat stomach and lean hard thighs. He wore the modified Cretan costume of black riding breeches and burnished high black leather boots. His white, narrow-collared shirt was unbuttoned almost to the waist, and showed off his muscular chest sprinkled with black hair. A gleaming gold buckle fastened his wide leather belt. His eyes were closed, as if in an ecstasy of voluptuousness. He looked like a pagan god.

A mixture of fear and ... something else ... an emotion she didn't recognise, flooded Lorna. She couldn't take her eyes off him. It was as if a Minoan prince had sprung to life from the ancient ruins on the hill below. A prince who danced before a shepherdess he intended to ravish.

The music grew wilder and he executed a complicated leap, his body leaned sideways in the air as he fetched his right hand down to slap both his flying heels. His head was thrown back so that the strong column of his throat showed clearly. He landed gracefully back on his feet, opened his eyes, and looked straight into Lorna's. His eyes were green as the mountain river, and were filled with provocation. His sensual lips curved slightly in a mocking smile. Without faltering in his dance he reached for a plate from one of the tables and dashed it to the floor.

Now the rhythmic thrusting of his hips was slow and sinuous. Lorna felt as if he was making love to her in full view of everyone in the café.

Until now she had succeeded in blending into the background unnoticed, but now she was the focus of attention. If he had trained a spotlight on her he couldn't have made her more visible. In the darkness she could feel the men grinning at her discomfiture.

Her cheeks burned with mortification, but she refused to lower her eyes. For she sensed that this was a contest. That if she looked away, in some obscure way she would have conceded defeat to this arrogant male animal. And she wasn't about to do that! She was filled with a slow burning hatred of this man, and she had no intention of letting him win whatever game it was they seemed to be playing.

It felt like hours to Lorna, but at last the music faded and her tormentor—for she had begun to think of him as that—stopped his sensual dance and dropped his arms to his sides. He remained staring at her.

Lorna lifted her hands and slowly and insultingly clapped them together three times. Then picking up her drink she turned away from him with a gesture of contempt. However, she didn't dare sip her lemonade for she knew that her rage would make her choke.

She was aware that he'd moved away, but she still kept herself turned from the bar, so that when a tray was placed on her table she looked round with surprise. On the tray were two glasses of ouzo, a glass of water, and a saucer of roasted chick peas. She looked up into the cynical face of the barman.

'What is this?' she said, pointing to the tray. 'I didn't order it.' She pulled her phrase book out of her shoulder bag and started to leaf through it.

'I have ordered it. To welcome you to our village.' It was the tall Cretan who had danced before her so insolently who spoke. He came and stood by her table. The barman moved away with a knowing smirk.

Standing before her he seemed taller than ever. And rugged, with a broad chest and strong arms. His hair was glossy black, and she noticed that his light green eyes had golden flecks in them, so that they seemed to glow, like a cat's. He was undeniably handsome, but this merely added to her dislike. She mistrusted handsome men in general, and the behaviour of this particular specimen hadn't done anything to change her opinion.

She looked into his strange green eyes with hostility. 'I don't drink with strangers,' she said coldly and looked away.

Far from discouraging him, this seemed to make the wretched man bolder. He turned one of the little chairs around and straddling it leaned his arms on the back, regarding her coolly. 'In Crete there are no strangers,' he informed her, 'and to refuse my offer of hospitality is an insult.'

'Good,' she said, turning to face him, 'that was the general idea.' She got up to leave, but her dignified exit was marred since she caught the side of her forehead a sharp crack on the hanging oil lamp. She yelped in spite of herself, and her blue eyes filled with tears of pain and anger.

He was at her side in an instant, and before she had time to protest had eased her back into her chair. 'You have hurt yourself,' he said, leaning over her on the pretext of examining her brow. He was so close she could smell the animal warmth of him, see the length of his thick dark lashes.

'It's nothing,' she protested, 'just a little bump.' But he ignored her.

'There is dirt on your forehead from the lamp,' he said, and taking a clean handkerchief from his pocket he dipped a corner of it into the glass of water and made to dab her face.

She flinched away as if he was attacking her with a hot poker. 'It's nothing I tell you!' she said sharply, startled that her reaction to his proximity should be so violent.

He shrugged and handed her the handkerchief before seating himself back on his chair. 'You should clean it,' he said, 'the skin is grazed a little.'

Wordlessly she pulled her pocket mirror from her purse and dabbed at the wound. It wasn't much, but she realised she would have a painful little lump on her forehead in the morning. Neatly she folded his handkerchief—which she noticed was made of the finest cotton—and handed it back to him.

He waved it away. 'If you will not drink ouzo with me, will you accept another glass of lemonade?' he asked. His mouth lifted in a mocking smile. 'To calm you after your accident.'

'I don't want anything, thank you,' she said primly, 'I just want to be left alone.'

'*Mou Theos!* And in search of solitude you come to *this* place.' He indicated the dingy room with a jerk of his dark head. 'I find that hard to believe.'

'I don't care whether you find it hard to believe or not,' Lorna replied testily, 'it's the truth. I just came in to look.'

His eyes narrowed. 'To observe the *curious* Cretan peasants at their local customs, *ne*?'

'Something like that.' She was beginning to comprehend that this man was unlike the other patrons. He gave off an air of undeniable authority. His command of English was impressive, and his clothes were undoubtedly expensive. His snow-white shirt was cambric, and his riding breeches were exquisitely tailored.

'I am surprised that such simple entertainment should interest a person from your world,' he continued loftily, 'but no doubt you are slumming merely.'

'I wasn't until you joined me,' Lorna shot back, her eyes emitting blue sparks. She stood up quickly, this time without bumping into the lamp, and made her way to the door.

The mountains had been turned to silver by the blazing moon, and the air felt cool after the stuffy little café. She had only taken two steps when he was beside her.

'Where are you going?' he asked peremptorily.

She started walking down the moon-dappled road. 'None of your business!' she snapped.

He suddenly gripped her arm, stopping her in her

tracks, and loomed over her. Her mouth went dry with fear.

'Do not be more of a fool than you already are,' he hissed, 'this is not a good place for a woman alone. I have my car. I will drive you to where you wish to go.'

She noticed a cleared space beside the café where among some donkeys and *mikanis*—three-wheeled motor scooters which were very popular on the island—stood a gleaming white Mercedes, like an elegant ghost in the moonlight.

'I don't wish you to drive me *anywhere*.' She pulled her arm out of his grasp and made to pass him, but he blocked her way.

'*Mou Theos!* You spoilt women of America are all alike,' he said contemptuously, 'you wander at will, looking at the ... the *natives* as if you were at a zoo. But when, in your ignorance you overstep the bounds of propriety, you are offended that you are treated with disrespect.'

'For your information I'm not an American, I'm a Canadian,' she said hotly, 'and furthermore I wasn't aware that I'd "overstepped the bounds of propriety", as you so quaintly put it.'

'Did it not occur to you that a café of that kind is not a suitable place for a single woman? Unless of course she visits it for the purpose of finding herself a companion,' he sneered.

Lorna's fine-skinned cheeks grew hot in the night air. 'Is ... is that what you thought?' she choked. 'That I was looking for a ... a pick-up?'

He shrugged his wide shoulders. 'It is not unknown for pretty tourists to add a Greek lover to their souvenirs,' he drawled.

'I can assure you,' she said, her voice quivering with indignation, 'if that were the case you'd be the last man on earth I'd choose.'

'*Endaxi,*' he said grandly, 'it is of no importance. But I intend to drive you back to your lodgings before you lose your way in the mountains, so do not argue with me anymore, or I shall be forced to carry you bodily to the car.'

Before she could say a word he put his hand under her elbow and guided her firmly towards the little parking space. Since she had no doubt that he would indeed carry out his threat if she protested further she silently obeyed him.

Apart from asking her where she was staying, he didn't speak during the short drive. Lorna sat tense in her seat. The car was a new one. Its red-leather interior smelled pleasant, but the clock on the highly polished wooden dashboard showed past midnight, and she cursed herself for ever embarking on her moonlight stroll. Since she liked to be on the site soon after daybreak, she was going to be dead in the morning. Besides, she was feeling thoroughly put out by the high-and-mighty behaviour of this devilishly handsome man sitting at the wheel. She'd never met anyone like him before—and she hoped she never would again!

They slid to a halt at the front of the dark taverna. Before her companion had a chance to get out Lorna had opened her door and was standing on the narrow dirt sidewalk. She leaned briefly through the open window, her gilt-bright hair swinging forward in a heavy curtain.

'*Kalinihta*,' she said, omitting any 'thank yous'.

As she turned to go in a figure materialised out of the shadows and came unsteadily towards her.

'Lorna! Where have you been? I have been worried about you. You are a very . . . very . . . naughty girl,' said Nikos, stumbling heavily. He was quite drunk. 'Who is your friend?' He demanded loudly, peering owlishly at the car.

'For God's sake, Nikos, keep your voice down,' Lorna whispered, 'you'll wake up the whole taverna.'

'Why did you leave so . . . secret . . . er . . . secret . . . with not telling,' he said belligerently, 'you are not kind to your Nikos.'

Her unknown escort stepped out of the car and faced the weaving man. He spoke softly, but in a tone that brooked no disobedience. Befuddled, Nikos stared up at him, then his face twisted in bitterness and he turned to Lorna.

'Always he steals what I want,' he said, the whine in his voice rising, 'always he cheats me.'

The older man said something sharply in Greek, but Nikos was too far gone in drunken self-pity to heed him.

'You did not tell me you knew him, Lorna,' he went on plaintively, 'you did not tell me.'

'I don't know what you're talking about,' Lorna said, exasperated.

'My cousin. You did not tell me you knew him. And I wait all the night for you. But you drive in his car . . . ' he whimpered.

'Your *cousin*!' Lorna said, her jaw dropping. She looked at the tall man standing aloof from them.

He inclined his head derisively. 'Allow me to introduce myself,' he drawled. 'My name is Jason Peritakis.'

CHAPTER TWO

AFTER Jason Peritakis's surprising introduction, Lorna spent another half hour persuading Nikos to let his cousin drive him home. So that by the time she'd crept upstairs to her room, washed her face in the dark, and undressed as silently as possible so as not to wake Susan, it was later than ever. By now she could cheerfully have seen the entire Peritakis family at the bottom of the Sea of Crete.

Usually Lorna was bright in the mornings, but the following day she woke reluctantly and dragged herself out of bed. Her eyes felt gritty with fatigue, and her temper was short. When she reached the site the brilliant morning sun, which usually gave her such a lift, was giving her a headache instead. Now she fully understood why their director, Professor Spanakis, disapproved of any member of his team indulging in late nights during the working week. She knew she was in for a tough day, and the fact that it was entirely her own fault didn't make it any better. At least she didn't have a hangover. Unlike Nikos, who she assumed must be feeling ghastly since he was nowhere to be seen. Behaviour that would not endear him to Professor Spanakis, who viewed absenteeism for any reason short of death as gross malingering.

She went into one of the huts that had been built as a storage room and put her spare cameras into plastic bags to protect them from the dust, making sure that the bags were not entirely sealed, then placed them with her extra film in an insulated picnic box. She jammed a disreputable linen hat, discarded by her brother years ago, on to her sleek head, tucked a T-shirt that bore the faded legend Star Wars into

23

her frayed shorts, and went in search of Professor
Spanakis.

She soon spied his pear-shaped figure overseeing a
group who were carefully brushing dried earth away
from a set of steps that had been uncovered the
previous day. The director turned and greeted her.

'*Kalimera*, Lorna! The work goes well here. You
should be able to take photographs by noon.' His
dignified face beamed. It was plain he was in a good
mood, and Lorna felt some misgivings about spoiling it
with news of the loss of her dark-room.

When she had explained the problem he clicked his
tongue against his false-teeth reflectively. 'Hmm. It is a
difficulty,' he said. 'We can possibly rent a refrigerator
for the film, but a *cool* dark-room . . . that is less easily
resolved. However, I will make enquiries. Perhaps in
Iraklion? Although it would be most inconvenient . . .'
He patted her arm absent-mindedly. 'But I shall find a
solution. Never fear,' he assured her, before leaving to
chastise one of the fieldworkers who was not taking
enough care with the stairs.

Lorna went off to help Susan wash pottery shards
and sort them. A job that required painstaking
attention. 'What time did you get in last night?' Susan
asked, when they had settled to their task.

'Late,' Lorna answered laconically.

'Must have been,' Susan agreed. 'I waited up for you
quite a long time . . . with Nikos.' She wiped the bend
of a handle gently with a soft bristle brush. 'Do you like
Nikos?' she asked casually.

'Not particularly,' Lorna said, picking up a fragment
and blowing dust off it.

Susan's face cleared. 'I'm glad,' she said, 'I don't
think he's a nice guy at all. And he drinks too much. He
was *polluted* last night.'

'You're telling me! That was one of the reasons I was
so late.'

'You saw him then?'

'Yes. He was waiting for me when we drove . . . er . . . when I got back.' Lorna was suddenly cautious. Not that she wanted to hide anything from her friend, but she felt too tired and confused about her brief meeting with Jason Peritakis to go into details.

However, Susan was no fool. *'Drove!'* she said, her eyes turning to circles of surprise. 'Who were you driving with?'

'Nobody interesting,' Lorna said hurriedly, 'somebody just gave me a lift . . . that's all.'

'Somebody nice?'

'No, as a matter of fact.' She wiped a trickle of perspiration from her face, leaving a smudge of dirt on her pale cheek. 'Do you have an aspirin, Susan?' she asked, in an effort to both change the subject and to relieve her aching head. 'I've a rotten headache this morning.'

Susan fetched her a couple of aspirin and the subject was forgotten. Although the recollection of Jason Peritakis's erotic dance at the café still lingered in her mind. At noon the team stopped work and flaked out under a few olive trees to rest and eat their simple lunch, which usually consisted of bread and olives with some cheese. Lorna went to check the freshly cleaned stairs, and after consulting with Professor Spanakis she set about taking her photographs.

She took the detailed pictures first, lying down on the dirt floor to get angles of the steps, then went to take some shots from above. She decided that the upper level wasn't high enough for the effect she wanted. Nor was a tripod. So she poked around in the lean-to and found two straight ladders which she lashed together to make an extension. Carefully leaning the structure as upright as possible against the side of the excavated wall, she slung her camera round her neck and gingerly climbed to the top. It swayed rather alarmingly when she slid herself round so that her rear-end was against the top rung, enabling her to look directly down on to the stairs.

Focusing her camera she proceeded to take several shots from this precarious position. She had just decided that she had enough shots when there was an ominous creaking and the ladder tilted away from the safety of the wall and started falling, slowly at first then gaining momentum. Lorna gave a shriek, and professional photographer to the last, held her camera above her head in an attempt to protect it. She steeled herself for the crash she would make on the sun-baked earth, when a man leapt from one of the half-dug trenches and hurled himself forward to break her fall.

She landed on him with such impact that they rolled over and over in the dirt before coming to a standstill with the ladder on top of them. After the sound of a shower of pebbles there was a deafening silence. Lorna lay inert on top of this unknown man for a moment, then she tilted back her wide-brimmed hat and lifted her head in order to look at him.

A pair of surprised green eyes looked into hers. 'You!' exploded Jason Peritakis, 'it was you under that hat?'

Cautiously Lorna extricated herself from Jason and the ladder. 'What are you doing here?' she asked weakly.

'I own this land,' he said, 'naturally I am interested in the progress of this particular dig.' He pushed the ladder aside and climbed to his feet, making a futile effort to brush the dirt from his fawn-coloured riding-breeches. Then he put out his hand and helped her up. 'Are you hurt?' he asked.

'Never mind about me, it's my camera I'm worried about,' she replied. She checked it carefully before giving a sigh of relief. 'Thank God! It's all right.' She slid it back into its case, then glanced briefly at her dirty arms and legs. 'I'm all right too it seems, thanks to you,' she looked up at him, her eyes almost navy-blue under the shadow of her hat. 'You make a marvellous safety-net Mr Peritakis. Thanks.'

He paid no attention to this, but looked at her with

growing dismay. 'What do you do here?' he asked abruptly, and when she looked at him uncomprehendingly, 'You work here, *ne*?' he barked.

'I'm part of the archaeological team. Yes.'

'Doing *what*?' he almost yelled.

She answered with dignity. 'I'm the official photographer.' Her gratitude was cooling with each peremptory question. Even when he'd just prevented her from a painful fall he managed to annoy her with his autocratic manner.

'*You* are the photographer? *Mou theos*!' he said, turning away. Before Lorna had time to question his peculiar reaction Professor Spanakis arrived on the scene.

'What has happened?' He peered over the rim of the upper wall. 'Has there been an accident?'

'It's nothing, Professor Spanakis,' Lorna assured him, 'my ladder fell over . . . that's all.'

'Fell over? On to the stairs?' He seemed more concerned about his stairs than his photographer.

'No. On to Mr Peritakis,' Lorna said drily, 'but we're both okay. Don't worry.'

'You must be more careful, Lorna,' the director said, mopping his face as he came down the incline to join them, 'we cannot afford to lose you. There is too much work to be done.' He halted in front of Jason. 'So you have already met Miss McCann,' he said.

'We have . . . bumped into each other . . . yes,' Jason drawled. Lorna looked at him sharply. Humour was not a characteristic she associated with this handsome Greek. But there was a twinkle in those strange green eyes.

'Did Mr Peritakis have a chance to tell you of his generosity, Lorna?' Professor Spanakis asked. Lorna shook her head, which was starting to ache again. 'He has offered a room in his villa for use as a dark-room,' the director told her triumphantly, 'and not only that. He has most kindly extended an invitation for you to stay there also. That way you will be close to your work, *and* there will be an extra place at the taverna for one of the new arrivals.' He beamed at them both.

Lorna found her voice. 'It's out of the question. I couldn't possibly stay at Mr Peritakis's villa,' she said firmly.

'Ah! Do not concern yourself my dear,' Professor Spanakis replied, 'Mr Peritakis's mother resides there also. It is quite proper.'

'That's not the point . . .' Lorna started to protest, but the director was already on his way to another part of the site and merely waved a genial hand in dismissal.

Lorna turned on her unwilling benefactor. 'Why didn't you say anything?' she snapped. 'You don't want me under your roof any more than I want to be there.'

He looked down at her, his well-cut mouth disdainful. 'It is quite true that I did not know you were the photographer when I made my offer,' he agreed, 'but now it is done. It cannot be undone.'

'Of course it can. I never heard of anything so stupid.' She was irrationally furious because he had not denied that he didn't want her at his villa.

He leaned closer to her, his eyes glittering like glass. 'It is you who are stupid,' he hissed. 'Stupid and ignorant. Do you not understand that in Crete it is unthinkable that an offer of hospitality can be withdrawn once it has been made.'

'Well, if you think I'm going to accept your invitation just so you won't look bad,' she said, her dirt-streaked face pink with indignation, 'you've got another think coming!'

'Do not be tedious.' His jaw was set as obstinately as hers. 'It is all arranged. Professor Spanakis agrees. It is the best solution to the problem.' She took a breath in order to protest further, but he held up an imperious hand. 'Not another word! In any case, I shall make a point of staying out of your way. You will hardly ever see me, I promise.'

'That suits me just *fine*!' she gulped childishly.

'*Endaxi*. It is settled then. I will send a car for you tomorrow. You can examine the room I suggest for your dark-room and make a list of all you will need.' He moved away from her and she noticed that he still managed to look elegant in spite of the dust that stained his immaculately cut breeches and red silk shirt. He picked up his riding crop from the ground and tucked it under his arm. 'I would suggest you wash your legs,' he said looking at her critically, 'otherwise those cuts may get infected.'

She looked down at her smooth tanned legs and noticed some scratches that were bleeding. She had been so involved in her argument she'd not noticed them before. Now several bumps and bruises began to make themselves felt, joining forces with her aching head.

She started climbing painfully up the hill to the base-camp hut. 'Let me help you,' Jason said, putting out his hand.

'No thank you. I'm quite all right,' she lied.

'*Mou theos*! Never have I met such a stubborn female.' He made a step towards her and firmly took her arm. 'Is it your North American emancipation that makes you so disagreeable. Or were you born that way?'

She was about to tell him that if he found her so disagreeable all he had to do was go away, when suddenly her ears started to buzz, the rise of cinnamon-coloured mountains started to swim before her eyes, and she was ignominiously forced to cling to him for support.

Sensing her distress he put his arm round her waist so that he was half-carrying her. 'Do you wish to stop and rest a moment?' He sounded quite gentle.

'N . . . no . . . I can . . . make it to the hut,' she faltered.

'I think not,' he replied, and scooped her into his

arms in one strong movement. She pushed against his chest in a feeble protest but he ignored her, and strode up the hill as swift and sure-footed as a wild mountain goat.

Susan, writing a field report in the shade of the hut, looked up in astonishment. 'Lorna! What's happened?' she cried.

'It's nothing, Susie,' Lorna said weakly as Jason put her into the old garden chair that Susan had vacated. 'I had a little fall, that's all.' She took off her hat and dropped it to the ground. Her hair was lank, her clothes filthy.

'Do you have clean water and a cloth?' Jason asked the goggle-eyed Susan.

'We've got water,' Susan said, going into the hut and filling a basin from the water-bottles. Returning, she placed it on the ground beside Lorna. 'It's cold. Is that okay? But I don't have any kind of cloth ... except kleenex,' she distractedly held out a wodge of pulpy tissues.

'No, no. I have something,' Jason said, drawing a white handkerchief from his pocket. He dipped it into the cool water and started bathing the scratches on Lorna's mud-streaked thighs.

She snatched the fine cotton away from him. 'I can do it,' she muttered, 'I'm not feeling faint anymore.' Realising that she was being ungracious she tried to make amends. 'This is the second handkerchief of yours that I've messed up,' she said. 'I'll get them laundered and ...'

'Do not concern yourself,' he replied with a return to his former haughty manner. 'I shall see to it that I have a supply on hand during your stay here since you appear to be ... how is it? Accident prone.'

'I'm nothing of the kind,' Lorna protested.

Jason turned a smile of such devastating charm on Susan that she turned scarlet and started to giggle for no reason. 'Allow me to introduce myself. I am Jason

Peritakis,' he said. 'Miss McCann has recovered I think, for she contradicts me again. I will leave her in your care Miss . . .?' He raised his dark brows questioningly.

'H . . . Hunt . . . Susan Hunt.'

He took her plump little paw into his strong brown hand. 'Enchanted, Miss Hunt,' he purred. 'I think Miss McCann should rest this afternoon, but I am sure the suggestion should come from you rather than from me. Miss McCann makes a point of always doing the opposite of what I advise.'

'Oh! Sure . . . I mean . . . of course,' Susan stammered, awash in the Peritakis charm.

'Goodbye then, Miss Hunt. *Herete*.' The smile left his face and he turned to Lorna, nodded curtly, and strode away.

Susan sighed gustily. 'So that's Jason Peritakis. Wow! He's gorgeous!'

'I'm sure he'd be the first to agree with you,' Lorna said, slowly climbing to her feet and experimentally flexing her legs.

'You've got to admit he *is* handsome,' Susan remarked dreamily, a faint smile on her full-moon face at the memory of Jason's overwhelming charm.

'Handsome is as handsome does in my book,' her friend said rancorously.

'He carried you up that hill,' Susan persisted, 'I think that's pretty handsome, don't you?'

'All that takes is muscle. Besides I was faint. He couldn't have left me to collapse at his feet and walked away. Even Jason Peritakis has better manners than that.'

The clatter of hooves on sun-baked earth interrupted her. Below them, Jason Peritakis, riding a magnificent chestnut saddle horse, galloped away at top speed. His horse's tail flying out like a red banner.

'Will you look at that!' Susan breathed. 'He's like a . . . a cowboy in a historical movie.'

'There aren't any cowboys in Greece,' Lorna

snapped, thoroughly irritated. 'For heaven's sake, Susan let's quit talking about the wretched man. It's making my headache worse.'

Susan was immediately all apologetic concern. She found some band aids and produced more aspirin for her unfortunate room-mate. She then insisted on driving Lorna back to the taverna where it was agreed she would rest for awhile before developing today's pictures.

On the short drive back Lorna told her friend about her imminent move to the Peritakis villa. 'Oh! Lorna. You lucky thing!' Susan shrieked. 'The house looks *fabulous*. And it's cooler up the mountain.'

'And all my buddies are down at the taverna,' Lorna pointed out morosely.

'Yeah! But you'll be with us most of the time. Besides—the Peritakis villa!' she turned to look at her dishevelled companion. 'I'll miss you though, Lorna. I just hope my new room-mate doesn't turn out to be a creep.'

'I wish you were coming with me "Susie Q",' Lorna said, 'but it's all been decided over our heads.'

'I wouldn't worry about it,' Susan reassured her, 'I'll bet you have a great time. I envy you.'

Lorna smiled. 'No you don't, Susie. You're much too nice to feel envious.'

'Don't count on that,' Susan grunted. 'When I think of you under the same roof as that gorgeous man I feel quite jealous.'

'You don't need to.' Lorna reacted sharply. 'All Jason Peritakis and I feel for each other is hearty dislike.'

The older girl braked in front of the taverna before turning to her passenger. 'You may dislike him, Lorna,' she said, 'but he sure doesn't feel the same way about you.'

Lorna laughed weakly. 'You're suffering from a touch of the sun my friend,' she said, 'you've been out among the ruins too long.'

'Oh no!' Susan replied doggedly. 'He likes you a lot. Just you wait and see.'

'I won't hold my breath.' Lorna climbed out of the car. 'And let's make a pact, Susie. Let's try to stay off the subject of Jason Peritakis for at least twenty-four hours. Okay? He gives me a pain.'

'Where?' Susan screamed. 'In your heart?' And she drove away in a cloud of dust.

After a long night's sleep Lorna felt as good as new. She removed the band aids from her cuts and covered her scratches with a full skirt of multi-coloured cotton, which she teamed up with a favourite low-cut purple T-shirt. Her freshly washed hair was platinum bright in the early sunshine, and her eyes sparkled as blue as the cloudless sky.

When she came down to breakfast she discovered Nikos sitting under the plane tree drinking a cup of Greek coffee. He still looked faintly haggard from his recent debauch.

'Morning Nikos!' Lorna said cheerfully, sitting opposite him at the long table.

'Is it true what I hear?' he asked. 'That you go to stay at my cousin's house?'

'Quite true. Professor Spanakis arranged it yesterday.' She poured honey into the dish of yoghurt Vasily placed in front of her. 'So you'll get your 'fridge and your room back soon Vasily,' she said.

'I am already knowing, Miss Lorna,' her landlord told her, 'I have sadness to see you leave the taverna . . . but . . .' He shrugged his shoulders expressively.

'You'll still be seeing a lot of me,' Lorna assured him, 'I'll only be sleeping up at the villa.'

'Why did you not refuse to go, Lorna?' Nikos muttered, after Vasily had left them.

'Why on earth should I?' She stirred the honey around her bowl of yoghurt in amber swirls. She was damned if she was going to tell Nikos that she had tried to refuse, and had been ignored.

'You do not have to sleep under *his* roof,' he said slyly.

Lorna chose to ignore the innuendo. 'It was all decided between Professor Spanakis and your cousin. It's really none of my business how things were arranged ... nor yours,' she added pointedly, applying herself to her breakfast. Nikos took the hint, and since the rest of their colleagues began to arrive at the breakfast table, she managed to avoid any more direct conversation with him.

Lorna's coming departure was now common knowledge, and she was the centre of much good-natured teasing ... tinged in some cases with jealousy. She realised it would be futile to try and explain to them that she would much rather be staying on at the taverna, so she merely smiled and let their banter flow around her like sea foam.

When they arrived at the site for the morning's work it was immediately apparent that something was wrong. They were told by Professor Spanakis's assistant that they were to go to the shed where the cleaned shards and other finds were stored before being sent to the laboratory in Iraklion. The director was waiting for them there, and had something to say to the entire team.

After the bright sunshine it seemed gloomy in the temporary building, but although it was still early the corrugated roof gave off heat, so that Lorna felt like a cake in a bake oven. And the dirt floor, disturbed by their feet, rose in a haze of dust, stinging their eyes and catching at their throats.

Professor Spanakis stood, a grave portly figure, by the long trestle table on which freshly washed pieces of pottery and fragments were laid out on mats before being stored in boxes and bags for the journey to Iraklion. There was an uneasy murmur from the young fieldworkers, then the professor cleared his throat and silence fell.

He spoke first in Greek, and although Lorna was becoming more familiar with the language every day, it was too fast for her to follow. Whatever he said had a galvanising effect on the Greek members of the team. A gasp went round the stuffy little room, and people turned to each other in dismay. The director held up his hand for quiet.

'Now I will address the English-speaking members of the dig,' he said. 'You will recall the two seal stones that were discovered last week?' Lorna remembered them well. She had photographed them when they had been cleaned of their centuries-old crust of dirt. Exquisite examples of Minoan miniature work. One stone was chalcedony, carved with a tiny, perfect ship. The other, slightly chipped on one side, was cornelian and bore the impression of an olive spray on its oval surface. 'Last night, when I came to pack our latest findings for shipment to the laboratory,' the Professor continued, 'I opened the box containing the seal stones to find it empty.' There was a shuffling of feet on the dirt floor, and a collective sigh of shock. 'On closer inspection I noticed that the box had been carefully prised open, then re-sealed in such a way that the theft ... for I regret that it is undoubtedly a theft ... would not be immediately noticeable. As you are all aware there is a black market for such antiquities. However,' he paused, and regarded his team with a stern face, his thick glasses glinting in the dim atmosphere, 'however, I am sure you are also aware of the penalties involved. The government of this country regards such crimes very gravely indeed. I do not have to tell you how I feel about it. Not only is it wilful plundering of our country's history, it also destroys the morale of the entire team. Because of the action of one ... or several ... of you, all are under suspicion. This, for me, is the most unfortunate aspect of the whole business. So I have decided to give the thief a chance ... a chance he or she does not deserve.' He looked silently for a moment at his assembled workers. 'I will give the culprit forty-eight hours to return the seal stones,' he said finally, 'and I will keep his identity secret. But if the stones are not returned I shall call in the authorities, and when the criminal is apprehended,' he drew himself up, and in spite of his rotundity managed to look tall and impressive, '*as he will be*! I shall see to it that he receives the maximum punishment the law bestows.' There was a general stir, and one of the students coughed nervously. 'You may now go to your duties,' the director said, 'and I urge the guilty one to think over carefully what I have said.'

Very subdued they filed out of the building. Outside Lorna joined Susan and several other members of the team.

'What a mess, eh Lorna?' Susan's moon face was crumpled with distress. 'Who could have done such a thing?'

'Lord knows.' Lorna fell into step with the others. 'I just hope whoever it is has the sense to return the stones.'

One of the Swedish boys spoke up. 'Maybe they were taken for a souvenir only,' he said, 'and so will not be sold on the black market.'

'If people want souvenirs they can take discarded or duplicate shards at the end of the dig,' Lorna pointed out, 'they don't have to lift two of the most valuable small finds we've dug up so far. No. I'm afraid it's a mercenary theft, not a sentimental one.' She kicked at the dusty track with her narrow sandalled foot. 'But it's a rotten deal . . . for all of us. I only hope it sorts itself out.'

Gloomily the group went off to their various tasks— the Swedish and American boy to sieve for small objects trapped in the dirt, and the others to start work on clearing debris from a wall at the far side of the dig. Lorna had no particular photographs to do, so she offered to help her room-mate with a routine chore

around the site. That of putting strings on tags.
Necessary but boring. They were working on this when
Lorna was told that a car had come to take her to the
villa.

'Lucky beast!' Susan said, as Lorna hastily grabbed
her camera, for she never knew when she might need it.

'Don't fret "Susie Q" ', Lorna said, 'I'll bring you
back a full description of the palace.' She put an
oversize pair of sunglasses on her pert nose and made
her way to the waiting car.

She was relieved to discover it wasn't the white
Mercedes but a dignified black sedan, driven by a
liveried chauffeur. They exchanged pleasantries in
Lorna's cautious Greek, then drove without further
attempts at conversation. The chauffeur drove fast,
blithely seeming to ignore the hairpin turns in the road
which climbed steeply beside stony fields that fell away
from the mountain. On a far outcrop of rock she could
see a church, whitewashed and dazzling against the
sunbleached hillside. At some corners of the road she
noticed small wayside shrines. Little boxes of stone or
tin with a glassed front, through which she could see a
small oil lamp burning, pale in the sunshine, like the
white heart of a rose.

The car turned off the road on to a paved track
flanked by two huge limestone pillars and started to
descend gently. Bright magenta flowers, like enormous
furry daisies, grew in a riotous carpet on each side of
the path. Oleander bushes massed in a profusion of
pink and cream blossoms, and the scent of dittany and
wild thyme filled her nostrils. The drive widened, turned
once and then they were in front of the villa. Lorna
caught her breath at the sight.

The house stood on a natural plateau that
overlooked the valley. Two storeys high, its honey-
coloured stone walls glowed jewel-like under the heavy
blue sky. On the patio two tall urns, shaped like ancient
Minoan *pithoi*, stood guard beside the glassed doors to

the cool interior of the house. Shallow steps led to a garden that was bright with flowers. There were several stone seats artlessly arranged under shade trees, and an oval swimming pool of Olympian proportions, which glittered in the brilliant sun as if it was sprinkled with slivers of silver looking-glass. Beyond the garden stretched a breathtaking view of the Peritakis olive and orange groves, enclosed on both sides by the mountain range that ended at the ocean shore.

Lorna was so enchanted by the magic of this scene that she did not notice the figure of a girl who got up from one of the lounge chairs by the pool, and came towards her.

'Miss McCann?' She was taller than most Cretan women, slim and tanned, with glossy shoulder-length black curls tied back with a piece of ribbon. 'I am Ariadne Peritakis. My brother asked me to welcome you.'

So Jason Peritakis was staying out of the way as he had promised. Lorna knew she should feel relief about this, but inexplicably she didn't. She felt mildly let-down. Like a child who has looked forward to a treat, only to be told she has to go to school as usual. She mentally shook herself and smiled at the girl, whose eyes were the same sea-green as her brother's.

'Thank you,' she said, 'I hope I'm not putting you to any trouble?'

'It is no trouble at all,' Ariadne answered, pulling on a cotton cover-up over her swim suit. 'It is a pleasure for us to be of ... of assistance ... all Cretans love strangers.' She dimpled suddenly, and the proper hostess was replaced by a shy young girl. 'And you afford me the opportunity to practise my English.'

'Your English is terrific,' Lorna told her warmly, 'if I ever get to speak Greek half as well I'll be very happy.'

Ariadne flushed with pleasure. 'I must tell that to my fiancé,' she said. 'He does much business abroad ... in

America. I will require my English for . . . for the entertainments.'

'I think you mean for *entertaining*,' Lorna corrected her gently. She had taken an immediate liking to this friendly child, who seemed so unlike her haughty brother.

The girl giggled. 'Of course . . . entertaining. And now if you will follow me I will show you the room Jason thought might be acceptable for your dark-room.'

She led the way across the patio to a path that went to the back of the house. After the bright sunshine the shadowed cool was like turning on an air-conditioner. They crossed a small courtyard and approached a stone building. Now Lorna could hear the sound of rushing water, and she saw that a narrow irrigation ditch ran alongside the path. Fig trees crowded the banks, and a tree that Lorna had never seen before stood before the door, its purple blossoms glowing in the shadows like votive lights.

Ariadne preceded her down two steps, opened the heavy wooden door and ushered her inside. She pressed a switch and a naked light bulb that was suspended from the ceiling gave off a harsh light. 'You see! You would have the electricity,' the girl explained, 'and my brother would see that water was brought in by pipes from outside. Of course it is very rough, with only a dirt floor . . . it was a storage room for many years . . . but we could arrange it to your requirements . . .' She looked at the Canadian girl.

'It's *perfect*!' Lorna said enthusiastically. 'It's so cool.'

'And remains so even in the summer's heat. The walls are very . . . wide?'

'*Thick*,' Lorna nodded, pushing her honey-coloured hair behind her ears and turning round to peer into the far corners of the low-ceilinged room. 'Oh! This is *terrific* Miss Peritakis,' her pretty mouth curved with pleasure, 'I'm most grateful to you . . . and . . . and your brother.'

'Endaxi!' Lorna's obvious delight was catching, and the two girls beamed at each other. 'Then let us go and have a cool drink while you make for Jason a list of things you will need.'

At the mention of his name Lorna's smile faded. 'There's no need to trouble your brother, Miss Peritakis,' she said, 'I'll give the list to Professor Spanakis and he'll get everything. There's a fund to cover such expenses.'

'I know,' Ariadne replied quietly, 'my brother has provided it.' Seeing Lorna's surprise she went on quickly, 'I tell you this so you will not feel under any ... any ... obligation to my family. I also would ask you to keep this information to yourself. It is not generally known we have financed the excavation.'

'I won't tell anyone,' Lorna assured her. She was not too pleased by this disclosure. It made her feel as if she was Jason Peritakis's employee.

They went to a corner of the patio that had a view of the hillside and the orange groves below. A vine had been trained over a trellis to spread a canopy of shade over a table and chairs grouped beneath it. Leaning back in the blue-and-white covered lounge chair, Lorna could see tight clusters of hard, unripe grapes, that would be plump and heavy with juice by the time September came.

'My mother sends her regrets that she is not here to welcome you,' Ariadne said while she poured them both glasses of ice-cold 'vissinada', 'but she had to go to Iraklion. There is still much to prepare for the wedding.' She tried to look blasé, but the hand holding the jug of cherry drink shook with excitement at the thought of her coming marriage.

'When is the great day?' Lorna asked. She looked out over the sun-drenched hills and idly noticed a cloud of dust moving towards them.

'In two weeks.' Ariadne bubbled over with eagerness. 'All the people of the village are invited. And the people from the dig as well are to come to the reception. We are all very, very happy. My fiancé's family owns a shipping line. It will be a good alliance for both our families.'

Lorna felt her liberated hackles rise. 'What about you?' she asked, more sharply than she intended. 'Will it be a good alliance for you too?'

Ariadne looked at her in surprise. 'But of course. We are very much in love, Kosti and I.'

'Well, I think he's a very lucky man,' Lorna said sincerely, hoping this would make up for her former sharpness.

'Thank you. But believe me I am lucky too. I have known Kosti since I was a child, and always I have been in love with him,' the Greek girl confessed shyly.

Touched by this confidence Lorna smiled at her young hostess. 'I'm very happy for you, Miss Peritakis,' she said warmly.

'Please to call me Ariadne,' the girl said, 'I feel we are friends, and surely friends are not so formal?'

'No, they're not. My name is Lorna.'

The two girls shook hands solemnly, then Ariadne laughed gaily. 'And now we are friends for life. That is the way in my family. We are constant in our affections.' Lorna didn't feel she had known her new friend long enough to enquire if this constancy applied to their antagonisms as well, so she merely smiled and sipped her 'vissinada'.

By now Lorna could see that the dust cloud she'd noticed earlier had materialised into a figure on horseback galloping towards them. She could hear the thud of the horses hooves on the rock-hard earth. Horse and rider disappeared from view behind a jagged rock, then reappeared just below the house, and now she recognised Jason, elegant in cream riding breeches and dark green shirt, the wind raking his black hair off his forehead as he galloped home.

Trying not to appear obvious Lorna gathered her

purse and camera and rose to go. 'Thank you very much for the drink, Ariadne,' she said, 'and for showing me the dark-room. I'll make out a list and get it to you by tomorrow.'

However, Ariadne wasn't about to let her escape. 'No wait, Lorna,' she said, 'Jason has just arrived. He will take you back to the site.' Lorna made some weak excuse about it only being a mile, and she needed a walk, but Ariadne refused to listen. 'A walk in *this* heat? No Lorna. Jason will drive you back. He will be happy to do it.' Lorna doubted this, but she sat down again and kept quiet.

A few minutes later Jason joined them, his hair still tousled from his gallop. He gave Lorna a formal little bow, then flung himself into one of the chairs opposite her, looking at her intently all the while. She became uncomfortably aware that the hollow between her firm breasts was visible in the low neck of her T-shirt. She straightened in her seat in an attempt to somehow get the knit material to become less revealing, but it didn't seem to work. Jason's mobile mouth turned up slightly, and his eyes grew bolder. At last he withdrew his gaze and accepted the glass of 'vissinada' that Ariadne offered him.

'Thank you *kookla*.' His expression softened when he looked at his young sister. 'Well, Miss McCann,' the gentle look faded, 'will the old storeroom be a satisfactory dark-room?'

'Just perfect, thank you. I'm sure Professor Spanakis will be most grateful to you,' Lorna replied with chilling formality.

Jason raised his dark brows quizzically. 'And you? Do you also share his gratitude?'

A flush of irritation spread over Lorna's high cheekbones. Damn the man! He was succeeding in making her appear unappreciative. 'Of course,' she replied brusquely, 'I'm grateful for anything that helps me in my work.' She was conscious that this sounded discourteous, and she grew slightly pinker.

Jason regarded her coolly. 'How fortunate for Professor Spanakis that he is blessed with such a dedicated worker.' He turned to his sister. 'I think Miss McCann must be a perfect example of the liberated North American business woman,' he said derisively.

'And I think you should not continue to address her as "Miss McCann",' Ariadne said hastily, sensing the tension between them, 'her name is Lorna, Jason.'

'Lorna,' he repeated it, 'Lorna. A beautiful name. You will permit me to use it?'

'By all means, Mr Peritakis.'

'Come!' he mocked her. 'Surely it is considered inequality for me to use your first name, unless you call me . . . Jason.'

'Jason!' She rolled his name on her tongue like a disagreeable pill. 'Jason. Very well.' She stood up again. 'But now I really must be getting back to work.'

'Allow me to finish my drink, then I will drive you,' he said.

'There's really no need . . .'

'Mou Theos Lorna! Do me the courtesy of not arguing with every suggestion I make,' he snapped. He pushed his half-empty glass away and went on in a quieter tone. 'Even if you were to run down the mountain with the speed of a goat it will still be quicker by car. The scenery will still be there, waiting for your camera.'

'The light won't.' She glared at him mutinously, noticing crossly how attractive he looked. His green linen shirt was unbuttoned and a fine gold chain glinted against the crisp black hair on his chest. He exuded male animal magnetism—and she could have hit him!

'Etsi!' He got to his feet, exasperated. 'Do not let me keep you from your work for one moment more. Come! I will drive you now,' and he strode off.

Hurriedly Lorna said goodbye to Ariadne and followed him. Without a backward glance he made his way to the garages. The black sedan was parked nearby, but he ignored it, going instead to a workmanlike jeep that stood beside a red sports car. She could also see the pale shape of the white Mercedes, as well as a stationwagon. She wondered how many cars the Peritakis family owned. So many automobiles under one roof seemed a bit excessive.

Jason leapt into the jeep in one fluid movement and turned the key in the ignition, pointedly not assisting Lorna, who climbed into the passenger seat and put her sunglasses back on, trusting they would hide the anger in her blue eyes. For two pins she would have told him what to do with his jeep, but she reminded herself that he had solved the dilemma of the dark-room, and that her boss wouldn't be too pleased if she offended their benefactor.

With a vicious stab Jason stepped on the accelerator and the jeep roared along the flower bordered drive down to the road. Lorna was forced to cling to the edge of her seat as they zigzagged down the mountain, tyres squealing at every turn. The wind swept her short bright hair off her face, and she felt as if all the bones in her body were being rattled out of their sockets. Within minutes they arrived at the site and skidded to a stop with a screech of brakes. He switched off the engine and again the silence of the mountains, broken only by the ever-restless river, enclosed them. A dark-winged butterfly fluttered past.

'So!' he said, 'I trust I got you here in time.' He still seemed to be in a temper.

'Thank you,' she replied, climbing out of the jeep, 'a very skilful display of dangerous driving.' She wasn't in the sweetest temper herself.

'Were you afraid?' he asked.

Lorna, who had no intention of being patronised by Jason Peritakis or anyone else, answered him in an off-handed tone. '*Afraid*? Good Lord, no. I've always enjoyed fast cars.'

He glared down at her, a disappointed little boy

whose bullying wasn't working. 'I do not believe that is true,' he said.

She shrugged her slim shoulders. 'I'm not in the habit of playing games.'

'I think you are,' he hissed. 'I think you are not honest. You were not honest the other night.'

Astonished, she gaped up at him. 'The other night?'

'In the café. When I danced.'

'What are you talking about?' She was thoroughly bewildered.

'I am talking about your lack of honesty,' he said. 'When you rejected me the other night you were playing games with me. I do not enjoy that. It would have been more honest to have told me the truth.' His eyes glittered coldly.

She removed her sunglasses in order to look at him fully. 'The truth?'

'Yes, the truth!' he spat back at her. 'Instead of letting me believe I was displeasing to you, it would have been more . . . more honest . . . if you had told me that you rejected me . . . not because I was annoying you . . . but because you already had a lover.'

CHAPTER THREE

LORNA looked at him with open-mouthed amazement. 'You seem to have lovers on the brain,' she said finally.

'You do not deny it?' he shot back.

The slim thread of Lorna's self-control broke. 'Why should I?' Her voice was tight with anger. 'I wasn't aware that I had to account to you for my private life.'

He glared at her through slitted eyes. 'You are right,' he said, 'but when you are living under my roof I would ask that you do not flaunt your affairs. As you have doubtless discovered, in Crete we are not as ... emancipated ... as you are in North America. In my house I trust you will behave with discretion.' Before she had a chance to reply to this insult he had started the engine and roared away.

Trembling with impotent fury she joined her colleagues, who had stopped for lunch and were sprawled in the shade of a cluster of olive trees. She flung herself down beside Susan and savagely tore a piece of bread from one of the crusty loaves.

'Well?' Susan looked at her enquiringly. 'What's the villa like?'

'The villa is beautiful,' Lorna replied, her mouth set grimly.

Susan prompted her. 'Well? Go on. Describe it.'

'I can't. I'm too mad.'

Susan looked amused. 'Had another tangle with dreamy Jason?' she asked.

'*Dreamy*! You mean nightmare! He as good as accused me of being a scarlet woman.'

'No kidding?' Susan mumbled through a mouthful of firm anthotyro cheese. 'Did you set him straight?'

'Why should I?' Lorna crammed a black olive in her

mouth and chewed it furiously. 'It's none of his business how I live my life.'

'You have to understand that he's a Cretan,' Susan went on munching steadily. 'He's bound to be jealous. It's his nature.'

'I know what his nature is. *Obnoxious*! I have never met a more infuriating man.'

'That's only because he fancies you,' her friend said placidly, swallowing the last of her cheese. 'If he didn't he wouldn't make scenes.'

'Oh! Don't talk such bloody *rubbish*!' She disposed of her olive pit, hurling it in an arc with unnecessary force. 'I hardly know the man.'

Susan began to methodically peel an orange. 'For someone you hardly know he sure gets under your skin. What's that old saying? "Methinks the lady doth protest too much."'

Lorna pushed her long slim fingers through her hair. 'I didn't mean to lose my temper with you, Susie,' she said ruefully, 'but everything seems to have become so . . . so difficult. First my having to move away from the taverna . . . and you. And then that rotten business about the seal stones. That's put a blight over everything.'

'Now there I agree with you,' said the older girl. 'But the person who took them may own up. Then everything will be okay.'

But Susan was overly optimistic. The forty-eight hours passed and no one came forward. The pall of gloom hanging over the archaeological dig grew. People found themselves staring speculatively at each other, asking the silent question—'Are you the one?' And their meal times, formerly so noisy and cheerful, became withdrawn affairs, with small knots of friends trying not to look suspiciously at their neighbours. Professor Spanakis had called in the authorities and every member of the dig had been questioned and their rooms searched. As the director had foreseen morale was at an all-time low.

Lorna found the general dejection catching. And added to this she had an additional problem. Not a serious one, but a problem nevertheless. It didn't take much imagination to figure out that Jason must think she was having an affair with Nikos, and she had a shrewd idea that Nikos, in his drunken ramblings the other night, had planted that particular seed. She couldn't decide how to handle this. The prospect of a confrontation with Nikos didn't thrill her, but she didn't see any alternative.

The evening after the police had made their enquiries she worked later than usual, so that she was the last to leave the site. Hanging her cameras around her neck she started down the road in the lavender-coloured dusk when she heard her name being called, and Nikos came running down from the storage hut.

'Lorna, wait!' He caught up with her on the dusty path. 'Do you go to the taverna? I will walk with you.' They fell into step, and after she had refused his offer to carry her cameras they started to chat. 'It is a pity that I no longer have a car,' he said, 'otherwise I would drive you, and we would not be forced to walk through the dirt like peasants.'

'I don't mind walking through the dirt,' she smiled, kicking at the path with her slender feet. 'Anyway, there's so much dirt on me at the end of the day another layer or so won't make much difference.'

Her companion ignored this. 'I too had a fine car . . . like Jason. You should have seen it, Lorna. It was red . . .' He trailed off wistfully.

'What happened to it?'

He slid his black eyes to look at her in the thickening twilight, then he said, 'I can no longer have a car.'

'That's too bad.' She assumed that he couldn't afford to run one, and remembering the fleet of automobiles in the Peritakis garage felt a stab of sympathy. 'Never mind! You'll have another car one day.'

He gave her another oblique look. 'Do you have a car? In Canada?'

'I sold it. I'll get another one when I go home I guess. Once I find another job. And get my furniture out of storage.'

'You sound so rich Lorna. To have furniture to store,' his mouth twisted with envy, 'you are lucky.'

'Yes. I'm lucky. But it's no big deal. My furniture consists of a bed, an armchair, and some dining-room stuff. It's stored in a friend's basement at the moment.' She resented having to apologise for the things she'd worked hard for. 'You have a house,' she reminded him, 'it must have furniture in it.'

He snorted derisively. 'Ah! The house belongs to my cousin. And my furniture is ... nothing. Shabby rubbish. I should be living in a house like the villa. Not a peasant's hovel.'

Oh Lord, here we go again! Lorna thought wearily. 'It didn't look like a hovel to me,' she said, remembering the two-storeyed house that had been pointed out to her.

She could just make out Nikos's face in the gathering dark, and she was struck by the difference between him and his cousin. She had never noticed it so clearly before. And it had nothing to do with the fact that Nikos was smaller, or that his eyes were brown. It was the weakness in his face that made him look like a man from another race. He looked blurred. Like an out-of-focus photograph. There was nothing out-of-focus about Jason. *His* face was as strong as granite. And as unyielding. But she had to admit that if she were to choose the one that attracted her, Jason would win hands down.

Nikos had left the topic of his housing, and was now going on about the police investigation. He was very belligerent. 'Why those pigs bother us I do not know,' he said. 'In any case they will never find out who took the stones.'

'I certainly hope they will. I'd hate to think of someone getting away with that.' As usual Nikos was beginning to get on her nerves.

'How do we know they have been stolen? Perhaps they have been lost only. And in the meantime we are insulted by the police for nothing.'

She said sharply, 'Well the police didn't insult me.'

'Ah, Lorna!' He stopped and grabbed her arm. 'Why do we quarrel? It is so silly. We do not care about the seal stones. I have a good idea. Let us go to my house instead of the taverna. I have a bottle of raki . . . we will have some drinks . . . play some records . . .'

She freed herself from his grasp and said firmly, 'No thank you, Nikos. I have a lot of work to do this evening.'

'You work too much, Lorna. Come with me to my house. I will make you forget working.' He lunged towards her and tried to kiss her mouth, but she was too quick for him. Bringing her foot up sharply she caught his shin hard with the side of her sandal. He gave a cry, and took a step backwards.

'Now just cool it, Nikos,' she said, 'and let's get one thing straight. I'm not interested in any kind of romantic adventures, I'm here to work. So please don't spoil our friendship by making passes . . . and don't spread any more rumours.'

He looked at her guiltily. 'Rumours! I do not know what you mean.'

'I think you do.' She looked at him steadily. 'Cut it out, eh? Now let's get down to the taverna. I'm famished.'

To her relief he didn't protest, but walked sulkily beside her, grumbling all the way. The gist of his complaint seemed to be that he was the most magnificent lover in Greece, and she didn't realize what she was missing by turning him down. By the time they had reached their destination she was heartily sick of him. Fortunately at dinner she managed to find a seat at the opposite end of the table, and so was spared more of his moaning, and by the time coffee was served he was well into the retsina, and didn't notice when she left to go to work in her new dark-room at the villa.

She'd been developing her pictures there for the past few evenings. The Peritakis family seemed to be away. In any case the only person she saw on these expeditions was the chauffeur, who insisted on driving her back to the taverna each night.

The dark-room was a huge success. The single window had been provided with a heavy curtain, and water had been piped in to a splendid new sink. She had been supplied with a refrigerator; a kettle; and an electric hot-plate. A sturdy trestle table had been built down the entire length of one wall, so she had plenty of working space. There was even a wicker chair with a faded cretonne cushion; a pottery mug; matching sugar basin and spoon; and a fresh jar of instant coffee. This final touch she felt sure had been provided by Ariadne.

This particular evening she worked later than usual, enlarging some colour prints. Coming out into the velvety night, the moon like a circle of pale frosted glass in the sky, she glanced in the direction of the pool and saw the figure of a man poised on the diving-board. He stood motionless for a moment, his body silvered by moonlight, then he dived into the water leaving scarcely a ripple on the mirror-smooth surface. He swam to the edge and with one lithe movement pulled himself up on to the flagstones and shook the water from his hair with the unconscious grace of an animal. It was Jason. She recognised him immediately. No one else moved with such elegance.

Holding her breath she started to creep across the patio on her way to the garage, but fate was against her. She tripped on a flagstone and her shoulder-bag fell to the ground with a thump. He called out something in Greek, and flinging a towel round his powerful shoulders bounded up the shallow steps.

'It's all right! It's only me,' she said, kneeling to retrieve the contents of her bag.

He gave a breathless laugh. 'You startled me. I thought I was alone here.' He knelt to assist her and she could see drops of water glistening in the dark hair on his chest.

'I've been working in the dark-room.' She suddenly remembered that she was still angry with him. 'I'm by myself,' she said crisply, 'no lovers in tow.'

He squatted back on his heels and looked at her gravely. 'I have only this moment arrived from Iraklion. I stopped first at the taverna. I wanted to see you.'

Kneeling down so close to him she was overwhelmingly conscious of the contours of his body in the brief swimming trunks, the scent of his firm brown flesh. Hastily she stood upright, ramming the last of her belongings in her bag. 'Well here I am!'

He stood too, and held out a pink plastic comb which she took and dropped into her purse. 'I wanted to apologise to you,' he said simply, 'I had no right to speak to you as I did. I am sorry.' His eyes never wavered. Lorna understood enough of the Cretan character to know how difficult it was for him to humble himself in this way, but she had no intention of making it easy for him, so she answered brightly,

'Don't give it another thought. I haven't.'

He released his breath with a hiss. 'How fortunate for me that you do not take such things seriously. I was afraid I had upset you.'

'You don't upset me, Jason,' she said, deliberately keeping her voice level. 'My life's far too busy to concern myself about other people's opinion.

'In that case,' he said silkily, 'you will not object to having a drink with me now. The fact that we are alone in my house will not disturb you.'

'It doesn't disturb me in the least,' she was determined to match his tone, 'but unfortunately I can't. Your chauffeur is waiting to drive me back. It wouldn't be fair to keep him waiting.'

His eyes glinted. 'How thoughtful you are, Lorna. However, I shall send him to bed, and when we have had our drink I will drive you myself.'

She was about to plead that it was too late, but she felt in some strange way she would be conceding defeat. Admitting that the prospect of being alone with him alarmed her. So she kept silent.

Smiling, he held her arm and courteously ushered her to a lounge chair on the patio. 'I will get our drinks myself,' he said, 'then if you will excuse me I shall change into dry clothes. Do you wish for brandy? Or ouzo? Perhaps some wine?'

'Some ouzo will be fine, thank you. With water.'

His teeth flashed white in a grin. 'A Cretan peasant would consider it fainthearted to add water to ouzo,' he said.

'No doubt. But when it comes to liquor ... I'm a coward.' She didn't add that somehow she didn't trust him. She felt she needed her wits about her, and the weaker the drink the better.

He went into the house and minutes later returned carrying a silver tray with two glasses; a bottle of Varvaressou brandy, and another of ouzo; a heavy cut-glass pitcher of water tinkling with ice-cubes, and a plate of 'mezethakia', the Greek equivalent to hors d'oeuvres. In this case roasted chick peas, olives, feta cheese and slices of brown coarse bread called 'karveli'.

While he went into the house to change Lorna lay back in the padded chair and sipped the drink he had poured for her. A little Cretan Owl called out from the sabled shadows, and in the lower garden the plane trees looked like great black-velvet umbrellas in the moonlight. She began to unwind. She was tired after her work in the dark-room, and the still night calmed her. She savoured the clean taste of the ouzo on her palate, and gently the tension slipped away from her body. When he rejoined her she was as relaxed as a cat. Leaning back against the blue-and-white cushions, one hand holding her glass, the other lying loosely along the rattan arm of the chair.

He stood in the doorway for a moment, looking at her. Then he said, 'Your hair is the same colour as the moonlight.' He had changed into jeans and a white shirt, and wore a pair of casual linen espardrilles on his bare brown feet. Sitting opposite her he poured himself a glass of brandy.

Hastily she straightened up and smoothed the skirt of her robin's-egg blue shirt dress. This caused her smooth fall of hair to swing like a silken bell.

'Was it always short?' he asked casually. 'Or did it once sweep your shoulders?'

'I had it cut for this trip ... to make it easier to manage. It was quite long before.' She felt as self-conscious as a schoolgirl on her first date.

'It is very pretty like that. It frames your face like the petals of a golden flower.'

'You mean I've got yellow skin?' she said, in an attempt to make the conversation less personal.

His voice was like satin. 'You know very well that I do not mean that. Do not be foolish. You are not un-used to receiving compliments, surely?'

'I get the odd one,' she agreed, draining her glass and putting it back on the tray. He started to pour her a second drink. 'No ... please, Jason. I really should think about getting back.'

'Why? Is someone waiting for you? Is that why you wish to hurry away?'

'No ... no of course not ... only tomorrow is a working day and ...'

'And I will not detain you very long,' he promised. 'Now come! One small glass of ouzo will not harm you. Particularly if you eat something. Look! You have not touched any of my olives.'

'*Your* olives?' Dutifully she took one and popped it in her mouth.

'From the Peritakis groves,' he said, handing her the

glass of clear ouzo, that started to turn milky the moment it was mingled with the water. 'Will you be here for the olive harvest?'

'When is it?'

'About Christmas time. The village olive press is on our land. It is a happy festival. My mother provides food and wine, and the whole village comes.'

'It sounds wonderful,' she said. 'It must be quite a job picking the olives though. It must take weeks.'

'We do not *pick* them.' He laughed, throwing back his head so that she could see the strong column of his throat. 'They are not oranges. We use sticks to beat them to the ground, where they fall on nets we spread beneath the trees. But you are right, it is a lengthy business. A good tree can take several hours to clear. Spring flowers are out before the last olives are in.' His eyes grew dreamy. 'It is a lovely season.'

'I wish I could see it,' she said, 'I'd like to photograph it.'

'For your album? A record of the quaint Cretan peasants.' The dreamy look vanished, and there was a sarcastic edge to his voice.

'That's the second time you've called the peasants quaint. Frankly I think it sounds damned offensive.' He didn't answer so she went on. 'One of the things that's struck me about the Cretan people is ... is an element of ... *nobility* ... I can't think of any other word for it. I'm sure life here in Crete isn't easy, but they are still the most generous and kind people I've ever met ... With one or two exceptions of course,' she added.

He smiled and raised his glass in acknowledgement of this barb, his even, white teeth dazzling. 'You are very observant. Most people come here in the summer months and see nothing but the towns and the coastal plains, where tourism helps to support the people. But here, in the mountains, it is a different story. The land is hard and the winters are cruel. At least in this village there is work for them in the Peritakis orange groves.

And the land is more fertile because of our river. So between working for me, and on their *kipos* they are better off than most other villagers. But it is still a struggle. Believe me.'

'What is a . . . a *kipos*?' Lorna asked.

'Each family in this district has a small plot of land . . . like a garden . . . which is called a *kipos*.'

'Like an allotment,' she butted in eagerly, 'we have them in Toronto. People rent them from the city.'

'Here they are usually inherited,' he explained, 'and between the wages I pay, and the oranges and olives we give to the village, and the food they can raise themselves, they manage to scrape a living. But when you see a peasant couple toiling on their little plot of land, remember that although it may look picturesque and make a charming photograph for your album, it is back-breaking work, borne with uncomplaining dignity.'

Lorna put her glass back on the tray. 'You're very unfair, Jason,' she said. 'You always assume that I look at your people through my lens and somehow . . . distance myself from them. But it's not like that at all. It's true that I've fallen madly in love with your country. It's as if I'm under some kind of . . . of magic spell. But I can still see clearly. I'm a professional photographer . . . remember? It's my *job* to see the truth.'

'And do you see the truth when you photograph our ancient ruins?' he asked.

'Oh! I see much, much more.' Enthusiasm swept away the last of her reserve. 'I *people* the dig. I imagine I hear the chatter of women on their way to market. In one house I can hear the creak of the wheel where the potter works. And then there's the baker's house, where grain is ground into flour and made into bread. I can almost *see* the frescos painted on the walls. Like the ones found at Santorini, but still vivid with colour, not faded yet by the years. And the shouts of children

playing on the streets ... and the barking of dogs.
When I put my eye to the view-finder the site is full of
life, and love, and beauty.' She stopped and gave a little
self-effacing laugh. 'You must think I'm nuts,' she said.

'I think you are beautiful ... and very surprising.'
His voice and eyes caressed her.

Whoa! Lorna thought, this won't do. He's beginning
to pay me compliments, and I'm beginning to *like* it.
Decisively she reached for her bag. 'This has been very
nice, Jason,' she said, 'but now I really must go.'

This time he offered no objections, and draining his
glass, rose and held out his hand. His touch was warm
and strong, sending pleasing sensations through her
own fingers. But once she was walking beside him she
gently drew her hand away. Again he did not protest,
but she felt him smile in the darkness, and she knew he
had guessed that his touch disturbed her. She silently
cursed herself for being so transparent.

He drove her in the Mercedes, with the sun-roof
pushed back so that she could see the stars above the
jagged peaks. When they were nearly at the taverna he
pointed to Nikos's house on the hillside, where a light
burned in a downstairs window.

'Nikos does not wait for you tonight,' he said.

'He doesn't make a habit of it any night.' She spoke
in what she hoped was an off-hand manner, but her
voice sounded strained. Once more he smiled, as if she
had made the right answer to some unspoken question.

She clasped her hands which had started to tremble,
for now the erotic tension that was generated between
them was beginning to unnerve her.

The car slid to a stop in front of the taverna. No one
was about. With one hand on the door-handle Lorna
turned in her seat to face him. 'Thank you for the
drink, Jason,' she said formally. 'I enjoyed it very
much.'

He switched off the engine. 'So tomorrow you move
in to the villa?' His voice was soft as smoke.

'That's right. I thought I'd move in the early evening ... if that's all right with you ... I mean ...' She heard herself chattering pointlessly. Her hand was still resting on the metal handle but it seemed to lack the strength needed to push down and open the door. He was a sorcerer, and he had cast a spell on her. She was incapable of action.

'You look like a moonbeam sitting there in your pale dress,' he murmured. 'A lovely silver phantom.'

'Goodness!' Her laugh crackled with panic. 'How fanciful you are, Jason. First you think I look like a flower. Now I'm a ghost ... believe me, I'm a very ordinary working girl.'

'Not ordinary,' he whispered, 'and not a girl ... A woman ... a very desirable woman.' He leant across her and gently detached her hand from its frantic hold on the handle, sliding his other arm across her shoulders. Softly he brought his warm mouth down on hers in a long kiss, at the same time adroitly pushing a button somewhere on the side of her seat, so that she was tilted back until she was lying horizontally, with Jason almost on top of her.

The spell was broken! She twisted away from him and found the button that operated the seat. In a second she was vertical again. But so rapidly that they bumped noses. Her lovely eyes filled with tears of pain.

'*Mou theos!*' He cautiously felt his nose. 'You are a mad woman!'

'You bet I'm mad!' She scrabbled around searching for her shoulder-bag. 'Mad at you.'

'But why? Is it not the custom in Canada to kiss good night?'

'Not lying flat on one's back!' She found her bag and started to open the door, but he stretched his arm across her and pulled it shut again.

'I do not understand you.' His eyes glinted in the dim light. 'By your own admission you are a liberated, modern young woman ...'

'Just because I'm modern doesn't mean I make love in the back seat of a car.'

'We are not in the back seat.'

Exasperated she turned on him. 'Don't play the innocent with me, Jason. You know damn well what I mean. I'm not wild about smooth operators, and that seat-tilting trick of yours is one of the smoothest tricks I've come across.'

To her surprise he chuckled with amusement. 'And for this you make my nose bleed?' He said.

'Your nose isn't bleeding.' She pushed his hand away and climbed out of the car.

'But surely, for a liberated young woman . . .'

'Something you "macho" types should get straight is the fact that being liberated means the freedom to say "NO",' she said through gritted teeth. 'Good night, Jason Peritakis.' With her back as straight as a ruler she went into the taverna.

Susan was sitting up in bed reading when Lorna came into their room. She put down her novel. 'What's up *now*?' she asked, as her room-mate started to tear off her clothes in preparation for bed.

Lorna pulled her kimono over her slim body and picked up her sponge-bag. 'Romantic encounters with *two* Peritakis males in the same day is proving too much for my temper,' she said, suddenly weary. 'At this rate I'm going to be a wreck by the end of the summer.'

Susan giggled and returned to her book while Lorna went off to brush her teeth. In the bathroom she rubbed cream on to her face, being very careful of her nose which was still a little tender. The ridiculous side of her latest clash with Jason struck her, and she grinned at her reflection in the fly-spotted mirror. She wiped the last trace of cream away, and traced the outline of her mouth with her finger, recalling the warm feel of his lips on hers. A faint echo of pleasure vibrated through her body.

Briskly she squeezed toothpaste on to her toothbrush

and started vigorously cleaning her teeth, as if with the taste of the pepperminty foam she could erase the memory of his kiss and her growing desire for his touch. It didn't work! She leaned in to the mirror.

'Damn you, Jason Peritakis,' she muttered, 'don't you dare become a problem.'

But in her heart she knew it was too late for such warnings. The spell had been cast.

CHAPTER FOUR

THE next evening Lorna moved into the villa. Ariadne
met the chauffeur-driven stationwagon at the door. She
held out her arms in a welcome. 'At last you come,
Lorna! I am so happy.' She was wearing a suit of pearl-
white raw silk, and her hair was pulled back in a shiny
knot. She looked more mature than the first time Lorna
had seen her, but the young girl still lurked behind her
eyes in spite of her grown-up suit and hairstyle.
Ushering Lorna inside she summoned a maid to help
the chauffeur with the luggage.

'We have only just arrived from Athens. And my
fiancé has just telephoned,' she glowed. 'His yacht has
just this moment docked at Iraklion.' Taking one of the
handles of the holdall Lorna was carrying she dragged
her up the wide staircase so fast that Lorna only had a
minute to register the low-ceilinged entrance hall that
contained several polished tables and chests of dark
wood. There also seemed to be a lot of vases filled with
bright flowers that flared against the white walls like
clusters of jewels.

Still chattering happily Ariadne opened a heavy door
at the end of the corridor. 'Here is your room, Lorna,'
she said, dropping the holdall and pulling her towards
the tall windows that overlooked the garden and the
orange groves.

'It's ... Oh! Ariadne ... it's gorgeous!' Lorna
stammered, turning slowly round in delight.

It was a big room. Big enough to contain a double
bed, a desk, a sofa, and an armchair, without any
feeling of clutter. The walls had been painted the
palest pink, and the lace-and-satin spread, gossamer-
silk curtains, and thick rugs were all cream coloured.

Near the windows a spray of leaves had been painted on the wall, so that it looked as if part of the garden had taken root in the cool room. The floor was ivory marble veined with pink. Standing on the dressing-table, which frothed with cream lace, was a large bottle of Christian Dior perfume and a silver bud-vase containing a single rose, whose petals were such a dark red they looked almost purple. A card with the word 'welcome' written on it was propped against the mirror.

Leading off from the bedroom was a small bathroom. A far cry from the primitive arrangements at Vasily's, the shower stall here didn't have a watering-can type of fitting let into the ceiling. It glistened with bronze taps and nozzles, and was enclosed in frosted-glass etched with a pattern of leaves. The tub was pink marble carved to look like a shell, and the fittings were bronze. A satin robe, the colour of coconut-ice, was hanging on a bronze hook on the door.

'For you, Lorna. So you will match your bathroom,' Ariadne giggled.

Lorna fingered the rich material. 'I ... I'm overwhelmed ... I don't know how to thank you.' She gestured towards the other room. 'This ... and the perfume ... How on earth did you find the time? With all the preparations for your wedding ...'

Her young hostess gave a self-deprecating laugh. 'Oh! I would like to take the credit. But I cannot. Jason got them for you.'

'Jason. Oh!' She dropped the folds of satin. 'How very kind. I must thank him.'

'He enjoyed doing it. Now hurry, Lorna! You are to join us for dinner in one hour. It is very informal. Just the family. You do not have to dress up.'

Before Lorna could protest that she didn't mean to impose on the Peritakis family, and had intended to return to the taverna to eat, Ariadne had heard the sound of a car arriving, and had danced out of the room.

The maid was already unpacking in the bedroom. She smiled and nodded, then went on efficiently folding and hanging Lorna's clothes. Lorna decided to have a bath in her shell-shaped tub and leave her to it.

There was a cut-glass bottle of bathsalts on the shelf, and talcum powder, and a marble dish of pink and white soap bars. She threw a generous handful of the bathsalts into the water, lay back in the rose-scented steam, and wallowed in the unaccustomed luxury.

Finally she climbed out of the cooling water and dried herself on a thick white towel. She put on her new robe while she dealt with her hair. It fitted her perfectly, Jason was obviously very observant. She couldn't decide whether this made her happy or not. But it certainly kept him firmly in her mind. In fact, lately, she seemed unable to think of anyone else. She savagely tugged at her comb, but didn't succeed in banishing the thought of him. She only hurt her head.

When she returned to the bedroom the maid had gone. Taking away an armload of clothes presumably to wash and iron. Lorna's discarded denim skirt and T-shirt had disappeared too. It looked as if she wasn't going to have to worry about laundry while she was staying here.

Ariadne had said dinner was to be informal, but she still dressed with care. She chose a favourite dress. A simple emerald green silk, with a pattern of lily-of-the-valley embroidered around the hem and cuffs of the loose three-quarter sleeves. She put on high-heeled sandals for the first time since coming to Crete, and wore large gilt hoop-earrings and a wide matching bracelet. She took trouble with her make-up too, shading her eyes with green shadow, and using a particularly luscious shade of coral lipstick. A generous splash of the Christian Dior perfume and she was ready.

As she walked downstairs she was irritated to discover that she felt nervous, so in an effort to calm herself she paused in the hall to admire a small statuette. A copy of the Bull's Head Rhyton (a libation vessel in the shape of a bull's head), from the Little Palace at Knossos, the famous excavation near Iraklion.

She traced the tight carved curls on the serpentine head with her finger. She had seen the original in the museum at Iraklion, and had marvelled then at the craftsmanship that made the eyes, inlaid with jasper, rock crystal, and white shell, gleam with life. She wouldn't have been surprised if this animal had snorted when she tickled his ears, he seemed so realistic.

'He is a fine beast, is he not?'

She nearly jumped out of her high-heeled shoes. Jason was standing silently behind her. 'Oh! You startled me!' She clasped her hands over her breast. 'I didn't hear you come in.'

He put out a hand and brushed her arm where the full sleeve had fallen back and she had to school herself not to gasp with pleasure at his touch.

'I am sorry, Lorna,' he said, 'I did not mean to frighten you.'

She smoothed the silk sleeves down over her arms, as if to protect herself. 'That's all right. I was just admiring this lovely head. Who did it?'

'A friend of mine in Athens. He specialises in copying treasures from the past. It is too bad he will be unable to copy the seal stones. Professor Spanakis tells me they are still missing.'

'I know,' she said, 'I can't imagine anyone on the dig stealing.'

He answered absently, 'No . . . no.' She wondered if it was a trick of light that made his handsome face look suddenly so strained and anxious. Then he made an effort and thrust away whatever thought was disturbing him. 'You look ... and smell ... delicious,' he said, smiling at her.

'Entirely thanks to you. The perfume's lovely ... and the robe. Ariadne tells me you're responsible. It's so nice of you, Jason. But you really didn't have to ...'

He interrupted her. 'Ah! But I did. It is to welcome you ... and to hope that I am forgiven for my ... clumsiness ... last night.' His mouth tilted wryly. 'My second apology in twenty-four hours.'

'You're forgiven,' she smiled.

'Then let us join the others.' He took her arm, 'My mother is impatient to meet you.' Opening a door he led her into a brightly lit drawing room.

The first person Lorna noticed when she went in was a dignified, middle-aged woman sitting in a brocaded armchair. She was dressed stylishly in black, a double rope of pearls gleaming round her neck. Her iron grey hair was piled high on her head, and her green eyes, so like Jason's and Ariadne's, studied Lorna intently.

Jason introduced Lorna to his mother and Madam Peritakis held out a strong white hand which glittered with rings. 'Welcome to my house, Miss McCann,' she said in careful English. Her handshake was warm, but her eyes, while not unfriendly, were cool and appraising, and Lora sensed that Katerina Peritakis did not intend to immediately accept this stranger in her midst.

'Thank you very much for your hospitality, Madam Peritakis. I'm sure you realise that you're a lifesaver,' Lorna said.

Jason's mother bowed her head in acknowledgement. 'It is nothing. It is our pleasure to have you here.'

'Still ... I'm aware how busy you are at this time. With the wedding arrangements ...'

'It is nothing,' Madam Peritakis repeated. She waved her hand towards a brown-haired young man who had been sitting beside Ariadne, but had risen when Lorna came in. 'I think that you have not met my future son-in-law, Kosti Theoari.'

Kosti took Lorna's hand and shook it warmly. She judged him to be in his late twenties. Smaller than Jason—but then most men were. Nor did he share Jason's extraordinary good looks. But he had a nice face, thin and serious, with good brown eyes that looked out honestly at the world.

When the introductions were over and Lorna had been seated in a chair opposite her hostess, an aperitif called propoma, a wine flavoured with herbs and spices, was served, along with a dish of small kebabs on silver skewers, and a bowl of almonds. Lorna was very hungry, but Madam Peritakis's steady scrutiny made her curb her appetite, so after a kebab, that sizzled deliciously on her tongue, she restrained herself and only nibbled on a couple of almonds, praying that her stomach wouldn't rumble.

'Kosti and I are to have a party this Saturday, Lorna,' Ariadne told her. 'We would like it so much if you would come. It is to be on his yacht, and there will be many people there, and dancing . . .'

'Perhaps Lorna does not care for parties,' Jason drawled, swirling the wine around in his glass, 'I suspect she is too dedicated to her work for such frivolity.'

'Do you? Then you're dead wrong,' Lorna said. She turned to Ariadne. 'Thank you very much. I'd love to come.'

Kosti leaned over to take a kebab. 'I think you will enjoy the party, Miss McCann,' he said. 'There will be a band for the disco dancing, and other music also.'

'We are to call her "Lorna", Kosti,' Ariadne admonished him. She turned impetuously to the Canadian girl. 'You do not mind if Kosti calls you by your Christian name?'

Lorna smiled and nodded her consent.

Madam Peritakis said severely, 'It is true I believe that North Americans are more . . . more casual . . .

than we Greeks. Given names are used easily. And I have heard that in business offices in America often the men will not wear a coat.' Lorna wondered what this stern Cretan matron would make of her working outfit of cut-off jeans and sweatshirt.

'When the temperature becomes impossible I dispense with my jacket in the office, Mama,' Jason reminded her.

She brushed this aside with a wave of her be-ringed hand. 'Tell me, Miss McCann,' she fixed Lorna with a green stare, 'tell me of yourself. That you are a career woman I know. But what of your family? Have you many brothers and sisters?'

Lorna understood that this was to be an interrogation. There was no ducking it. Her hostess intended to discover all she could about her guest before she offered friendship.

'I have a married sister, and a brother who works for an oil company in Singapore,' she told her.

Madam Peritakis was not content with this. She wanted more details. 'And your parents?'

'My parents were killed in a car accident when I was fourteen. My sister, who is seven years older than I, came back home to look after us until she married. By that time my brother was in university, and I was studying to become a photographer.'

Jason's mother looked genuinely upset. 'My poor child!' she said. 'What a tragedy.'

'It was . . . a difficult time.' Lorna's wide eyes grew sad. Then she roused herself and said. 'At least I had my sister and my brother. We've always been very close.'

'And now your brother is away in Singapore?' The older woman persisted.

'Poor Lorna! So you have no brother to protect you!' Ariadne's face was a mask of concern.

Lorna grinned. 'That's right! I have to protect myself.'

'And you do an excellent job,' said Jason. He gave her a faint smile and rubbed his nose reflectively. Lorna stifled a giggle.

But Madam Peritakis had not finished her cross-examination even though her manner was warmer. 'Your sister?' she asked. 'You visit with her often?'

'She and her husband live in British Columbia. That's over two thousand miles from Toronto,' Lorna pointed out. 'I did go to see them last Christmas . . . I wanted to see my new nephew . . . but it's rather expensive, and Rab . . . that's Ann's husband . . . Rab's a doctor in a small town. He doesn't make enough to send them east to me.'

'You must miss them,' Kosti said, 'to be separated from those you love is hard.' He reached out and took Ariadne's hand when he said this, as if to reassure himself that such a fate wasn't about to happen to them.

'I miss them very much,' she confessed, 'but one can't have everything. I'm lucky that I have a job I enjoy. And can come to places like Crete. I love to travel, but I couldn't afford it if it wasn't part of my job.'

'I did not work, yet I travelled extensively.' Madam Peritakis sounded censorious, and Lorna was provoked into saying sharply.

'Did you travel alone, Madam?'

'*Mou theos*! Of course I did not.' The older woman looked shocked. 'I was always accompanied by my husband.'

'Well I have to settle for travelling with my work.'

Jason broke in. 'You must remember, Mama,' he said, 'in these emancipated times young women travel alone all over the world. Lorna would no doubt consider it boring to travel with a husband. Is that not so, Lorna?'

She looked at him coolly for a second before answering. 'You have the most peculiar views about emancipation, Jason,' she said finally. 'My sister, who is a nurse for her husband and runs his household, plus three small children, would laugh her head off if she heard you. I've always envied Ann,' she said to his mother, 'she and Rab don't have much money, but they have a terrific marriage. I don't think anything can beat that. Do you?'

'Indeed I do not.' Madam Peritakis's stern expression vanished and she regarded her guest warmly. 'I too was happy in my marriage. When my husband died . . .' Her eyes grew misty and Jason put his hand over hers. 'No . . . no.' She smiled. 'I have many happy years to be grateful for. And now . . .' She indicated Kosti and Ariadne. 'Now these dear children . . . this is a time for joy, not sadness.'

After a moment of quiet the conversation resumed and became more general. They discussed the island, and the differences of the towns of Iraklion and Chania. Kosti, the Athenian among them, praised his city to Lorna. Then dinner was announced and Jason led the way to the dining room.

There was an immense table gleaming with white damask. Candles in silver candelabras flickered, making shadows dance on the terracotta walls. At one end of the room was a fireplace, filled now with a brass filigree fan, that gleamed in the lambent candle-light. Cut-glass wine goblets sparkled, and bowls of roses glowed against the sheen of the tablecloth.

Jason sat at one end of the table, his mother on his right; Lorna on his left. Kosti reluctantly left Ariadne's side and was seated next to Lorna. Ariadne sat demurely beside her mother, glancing shyly at her fiancé through lowered lashes.

Their meal, though unpretentious, was a gastronomical delight. Small chilled bouillon cups of cold egg-lemon soup; roast squab stuffed with rice and nuts flavoured with cognac; cucumber and tomato salad; and a chilled Rodyts Rosé. After dessert—fresh fruit dressed with yoghurt and honey—they had coffee on the patio. Lorna refused the brandy that was offered, but Jason and his mother each took a small glass.

Tonight the moon was sometimes obscured by clouds which the wind sent spinning across the sky like scraps of cloth-of-silver. The perfume of thyme and rosemary filled the air. Lorna leaned back in her chair with a sigh of content.

'What a heavenly spot this is,' she said, 'when the moon comes out I can glimpse the sea.' She turned to her hostess. 'Have you always lived here, Madam Peratakis?'

'Not always. I was born in Chania. I came here as a bride. My husband's grandfather built the house. Before that generations of Peritakis farmed the land.'

Jason leaned forward and at that moment the moon came from behind a cloud. His strong face was washed with white light that accentuated the hard line of his jaw. 'The Peritakis orchards were started from a small family *kipos*,' he said. 'My ancestors built all this with their bare hands.' He gestured to the valley below. 'One day I hope to pass it on to my sons.'

Madam Peritakis's glass made a sharp click as she put it on the silver tray. 'You will have to hurry, Jason,' she said drily, 'you will be thirty-five on your next birthday.'

Ariadne giggled from the shadows where she sat with Kosti. 'First he has to see me safely married, Mama. In two weeks only will he be free to choose a wife.'

'These old traditions are surely dying *kookla mou*,' Kosti said, smiling indulgently at his fiancée. 'I am sure if Jason had wished it he could have married before this.'

'Indeed yes. I should not have stood in his way.' There was a hard edge to Madam Peritakis's voice, and Lorna felt pretty sure the conversation had drifted into dangerous territory.

Jason took his mother's hand and kissed it teasingly.

'But you know, Mama, that I am looking for a girl like you. To find such a one . . . it takes time.'

She pulled her hand away and slapped it lightly in reproof, but her face was alight with tenderness. It was clear this was a close-knit family, and for a moment Lorna felt a tremor of sadness.

She had not admitted to them how very much she did miss her brother and sister. Before her parents had died she had been the youngest of a boisterous, happy family. Then with a squeal of tyres her life had changed. All through those black months after the funeral she had clung to Ann and Simon like a drowning man to a raft. Gradually the shock and pain had passed, and life had resumed. Ann had met and married her husband. Simon had gone to Singapore, and Lorna had carved a niche for herself in her chosen profession. But always in the depths of her heart there was an empty space. Brought up to despise self-pity, she had buried her loneliness and flung herself into her work. But her need for love, and the security of a family was still there, lying dormant. Waiting to surface when she let down her guard.

Jason spoke her name softly, and when she didn't answer he said again, 'Lorna . . . Lorna would you like to come for a walk in the garden?'

'Sorry.' She shook her head, and her silky hair brushed her cheeks. 'Sorry . . . I was miles away. A walk? No . . . I don't think so thanks. I think I'll go and look at some prints I have drying in the dark-room . . . then I'll go to bed. I have to get up early.' In her weakened emotional condition a walk through the perfumed night with Jason was asking for trouble. If he tried to kiss her she was liable to respond with a hunger that might surprise him. Better play safe.

She had just replaced her delicate china coffee cup on the tray when there was a clatter of boots and Nikos came out on to the terrace. He carried a bunch of flowers, which looked suspiciously like the oleanders that grew along the Peritakis drive.

The atmosphere on the patio grew tense, and Lorna knew they were all trying to asses if Nikos had been drinking. When it became clear that he was sober she felt she could almost *hear* their collective sigh of relief.

Madam Peritakis welcomed her nephew in Greek and offered him coffee, which he refused. He noticed the bottle of Metaxa. 'Perhaps a little brandy?' he said in English.

Jason poured him a small glass and Nikos took it with a hand that trembled slightly. After a quick gulp he handed the bouquet of creamy blossoms to Lorna. 'For you, Lorna,' he said, 'to welcome you to my aunt's house. May you be happy here.'

Lorna found to her embarrassment that she was the centre of attention. Kosti and Ariadne seemed amused, Madam Peritakis was curious, and Jason looked on with an air of monumental disdain. 'How kind of you, Nikos,' she mumbled, 'I'm being thoroughly spoiled this evening.'

'I expected to find you working hard in your dark-room,' Nikos said. 'I went there first. I was sure you would be there.' He addressed the group. 'Naughty Lorna works far too hard,' he informed them. 'I am hoping that now she has come to stay with you she will take more time for resting. You must insist on it Thia Katerina,' he said to Madam Peritakis, 'she needs looking after, I think.'

Lorna bit her lip. What on earth would the Peritakis think? 'I'd be grateful if you didn't talk about me as if I was some kind of half-wit, Nikos,' she said.

'But it is true,' Jason cut in, 'you work very hard. Why, just now you refused to go walking because you still wished to work in the dark-room ... which is where Nikos expected to find you.' His lips were thin with distaste, and with a sinking heart Lorna realised that he assumed that she had arranged an assignation. And from the way his green eyes were blazing it was clear he was furious.

Clasping her flowers she got to her feet. Jason's silent anger was unnerving and her legs shook under her, but she managed to keep her voice steady. She even managed a smile. 'After all this talk about how hard I work I suddenly feel exhausted. So I think I'll skip the dark-room and go straight to bed . . . if you'll all excuse me.'

Nikos immediately objected that he'd only just arrived, but Kosti got to his feet declaring that it was late and he too had to leave, so the party broke up.

In the hall Jason turned to his cousin. 'I am driving now to Iraklion,' he said, 'I will drop you off at your house. It is on the way.' And Nikos sulkily thanked him.

Lorna had just started to climb the stairs when Jason came up to her. He spoke so softly only she could hear him. 'I trust I have not disrupted your plans for tonight?'

She was standing on the third stair, so she was above him, looking down into his face which was lit from the hanging hall lamp. He was quivering like a strung wire, and his nostrils were dilated with rage. He looked like the minotaur about to charge. She said, as grandly as she could under the circumstances, 'As usual I haven't the faintest idea what you're talking about, Jason. And now you'd better get going. Your passengers are waiting.' He glared at her for a moment before turning on his heel to join the two men who were still waiting for him in the doorway, and shakily she made her way upstairs.

Once in her room she kicked off her shoes, collapsed on the sofa and said aloud—'Damn, damn, damn!'—What was the matter with Nikos? Surely she'd made it plain she wasn't interested in him? Why did he talk of her in front of others in such an asinine way? Did he think he would win her by such behaviour? Wear down her resistance like water on a stone?

And now Jason was livid with her, and she *cared*

what he thought. She finally had to admit it. She cared. Not that it could lead anywhere she cautioned herself. They came from such different worlds there could be no future for them. Besides, she knew he only wanted to make a conquest. Get her into bed. And he'd probably boast about it afterwards, she thought morosely, briefly indulging in an unpleasant day-dream of Jason bragging to his cronies at the café where she'd seen him dance that first evening. Firmly she banished this sordid picture. But in spite of the comfortable bed she slept badly that night, and the next day her eyes were shadowed. This led to a lot of good-natured teasing at work about her hectic social life 'up at the villa'. She went along with the gag, but for the first time since coming to Crete the day seemed endless, and she was thankful when it finally came to an end.

CHAPTER FIVE

ON the day of the party Lorna decided to go for broke. Ariadne had told her it was to be formal, so she unpacked a turquoise chiffon evening dress she'd only popped into her luggage at the last minute on the proposition that a girl should travel with at least one evening dress, just in case of emergencies.

When she'd bathed and made-up she surveyed herself critically in the long glass in her bathroom. Her dress was fashioned in the Empire style, cut high under the breasts. Two slender shoulder-straps held the bodice in place. She discovered that even the flimsiest bra showed, so she went without one for tonight, and felt rather wicked as a result. When she'd been in Athens she had bought a pair of low-heeled gold sandals with narrow thongs studded with turquoise-coloured stones. These not only went perfectly with this gown, but were very comfortable, which would be great for dancing, and Lorna loved to dance.

She looked good. The strong colour emphasised her tan and made her eyes seem darker, but something else was needed. She thought for a moment then went to her jewel-box and took out a small turquoise ring and matching bracelet that had belonged to her mother. She also found two enamelled clips for her hair. Shaped like butterflies, they matched the drift of white butterflies scatteringly printed down one side of her skirt.

She parted her thick hair in the middle and drew it back off her face, fastening it with the clips. This accented her high cheekbones and made her look more sophisticated. Satisfied, she picked up her evening purse and headed for the sitting room where they were to meet and arrange transportation to the party.

Madam Peritakis, stately in wine silk, was the only one in the room. She greeted Lorna warmly. 'What a very pretty dress,' she said, 'did it come from Canada?'

'As a matter of fact a friend of mine designed it,' Lorna told her. She described her previous job as a fashion photographer.

When she'd finished Madam Peritakis said, 'Your life has been so interesting Miss McCann. It must be very boring for you here in our village.'

'Oh no!' Lorna flushed with animation. 'I got dreadfully bored photographing fashion all the time, and spending all my time with people from that world. It may *sound* exciting, but believe me it's very unsatisfying and ... and shallow ... I can't imagine ever being bored here in Crete. Surrounded as you are by beauty, and history, and people who have more to occupy them than the latest styles from Paris. So you see,' she went on, 'this job is particularly great for me. In spite of the long spells of routine work on the dig ... and the hard slogging ... I still feel as if I've been released from a dreary room and let loose in a world that's full of magic.' The older woman smiled. 'I know that sounds a bit far-fetched,' Lorna said, 'but it really is the way I feel.'

'My dear child I do not smile because I find you amusing. But the ... how do you call it ... *similarity* ... of your emotions about your work ... and Ariadne's about her coming marriage struck me. She too speaks of being in a magic world.'

'Oh yes! The magic of love.'

'And have you never been in love?' Madam Peritakis asked.

'I've thought I was a couple of times. But never enough to get married.'

She remembered a conversation she'd had with her sister that past Christmas. 'The trouble with you, Lorna, is that you're just too choosy,' Ann had chided her.

'And what about you?' Lorna had challenged. 'You weren't choosy at all I suppose?'

'Me! Oh! I was just lucky,' Ann had grinned, and the discussion had been dropped.

'When the right man comes along you will know,' Madam Peritakis said firmly. 'There will be no mistaking it.'

At that moment the door flew open and a swirl of pale yellow net, the colour of ripe wheat, burst into the room. Ariadne dramatically held up a small nosegay of minute cream-and-orange orchids and addressed her mother in a torrent of passionate Greek.

At first Madam Peritakis answered her in that language, then she switched to English. 'Calm yourself, Ariadne,' she said. 'Lorna can no doubt help us. She tells me she has experience in the fashion world.' Her green eyes met Lorna's and both women acknowledged her use of Lorna's Christian name.

Ariadne histrionically held out the orchids. 'Oh! Lorna what shall I do? Kosti has sent me these, but they look awful on this dress. They are . . . swallowed up by it.'

Her dress was fashioned to fall off her shoulders in a deep frill, and indeed the flowers were lost on it. 'How about in your hair?' Lorna asked, but had to agree that that wouldn't work either. Ariadne's hair had been dressed high and braided and looped with a string of crystals. It was far too elaborate for the tiny bouquet.

Inspiration came. 'I've got it!' Lorna cried, and started giving orders as if she was taking photos on location. 'I'll need some wire . . . and some ribbon that will tone with your dress, and a needle and thread.'

A maid was sent for these articles and Lorna began to carefully undo the coppery flowers and delicate leaves. She smiled up into Ariadne's worried face. 'Don't panic. It's going to look terrific! I promise.'

When the things arrived she worked deftly. After measuring a piece of wire to fit the girl's wrist she sewed a length of velvet ribbon around it and stitched the orchids and leaves on to it. Then she bent it into a circlet for Ariadne's wrist. It looked charming and went with the flounced Victorian-style gown perfectly.

Ariadne was ecstatic. She held up her arm, admiring the pretty effect of the flowers next to her skin. 'Oh! Mama look! It is *perfect* I think.' She kissed Lorna's cheek. 'You are an angel, Lorna. And so clever. Is she not, Mama?'

Her mother patted her daughter's shoulder. 'Very clever, indeed. I certainly hope you will be close by when we dress the bride, Lorna,' she laughed, 'otherwise I am liable to have the nervous breakdown.'

'*Look*, Jason!' Ariadne flung herself at her brother, who had just come into the room. 'Look what Lorna has made for me . . . out of Kosti's flowers . . . Is it not pretty?'

'Very pretty *cookla mou*. And so are you,' he said, but his eyes were on Lorna, who stood motionless, a turquoise-and-gold flower against the white wall. Her heart fluttered under the thin chiffon, but she held her flaxen head high and gazed back at him without blinking, so that he was the one who was forced to lower his eyes.

He went to his mother and kissed her cheek. '*Kalispera*, Mama. Forgive me for being late. I did not finish work as soon as I had hoped.' Again he faced Lorna and nodded his gleaming dark head austerely. '*Kalispera*, Lorna,' was all he said.

She inclined her head in answer. Under the lights her hair looked like polished satin.

He addressed the three of them. 'Manolis is waiting with the limousine, Mama. I propose to drive Ariadne myself. I suggest that you and Lorna go with Manolis. That way there will be a car at your disposal should you wish to leave the party before us.'

'What of Nikos?' Madam Peritakis asked. 'Are we to wait for him here?'

'Nikos informs me he will make his own way to Iraklion.' Jason's face was like carved granite. 'So you will have to wait to see him at the party, Lorna.'

Lorna raised her delicate eyebrows, but all she said was, 'I had no particular plans to meet Nikos.' He looked at her sceptically, then picking up his mother's light silk wrap silently escorted the women to the waiting cars.

During the drive to Iraklion Lorna listened politely while her hostess described some of the guests she would meet, and their relationship to the Peritakis family. But her mind was brooding on that short, chill meeting with Jason just now. She told herself that it was just as well he thought she was involved with Nikos because that meant he would leave her alone, and that was what she wanted. That way she was protected from herself. Because she had to admit that she found him devastatingly attractive, and she knew she wouldn't be able to resist him. She knew herself well enough to recognise that a brief summer affair with Jason Peritakis would only make her unhappy, and there was no way it could ever be more than that. Much more sensible to let him think she was unavailable and wait for her infatuation to pass.

All the time she was giving herself this silent advice her heart sank lower and lower, and the moonlight seemed to lose its sparkle.

At the Iraklion harbour they found the area around Kosti's yacht—the *Calliope*—roped off. The whole place was ablaze with lights which were strung on the rigging, and also outlined the magnificent vessel. Her decks were thronged with beautifully dressed people. The women glittering with jewels and silks. Lorna tok a deep breath and headed for the ladies room to powder her nose.

A stateroom had been set aside for the ladies' use during the party. Lorna had a jumbled impression of mahogany panelling and apple-green satin, pot-bellied brass lamps, and deep pile carpet. Leading off from this was the bathroom, tiled in green with an ivory porcelain washbasin painted with mermaids, and gold plated taps shaped like dolphins.

Wow! she said to herself as she carefully re-did her mouth, you're among the idle rich tonight, my girl. Better *try* to enjoy yourself in spite of Jason. And she proceeded to do just that.

Kosti introduced her to a group of young men from Athens, all relatives of his. They all spoke good English, and they all took one look at Lorna and didn't look at any other woman for the rest of the evening. She was plied with champagne, given a tour of the ship, danced off her feet, and kissed once, by a particularly ardent admirer when he found her alone on the deserted lower deck where she'd gone to catch her breath.

It was pleasant being admired and kissed, and Lorna, like any young woman, enjoyed being made a fuss of. But something was missing, and she wasn't really as carefree as she appeared. Although she floated round the dance floor in the arms of a succession of partners, she was overwhelmingly conscious that it was Jason's arms she wanted round her; Jason's hand in the small of her back guiding her firmly. And if anyone was going to kiss her, it was Jason's lips she wanted to feel on hers.

In an attempt to deny this longing she laughed a lot, particularly when she noticed Jason watching her—which he seemed to do all the time—and she drank more champagne than she normally would have done.

She yearned to dance with him, and tried to will him into asking her. But he obviously didn't get the message, for even when she caught his eye, and smiled with brittle brilliance, his thoughtful expression didn't change, and he turned away and disappeared in the crowd.

The band took a break and she leant against the ship's rail, feeling the sea-breeze blow against her feverish skin. Her partner had gone to fetch her more champagne, and she was momentarily alone. Ariadne came up to her and asked,

'Do you have a good time Lorna?'

'Marvellous! I just hope my shoes stand up to all this dancing.' She poked her prettily shod foot out from the folds of her skirt.

'All Kosti's friends have fallen on you,' Ariadne said.

'I think you mean "fallen *for*",' Lorna giggled, 'and I think you exaggerate a bit.'

'Oh no!' She shook her head and the crystals in her hair glittered like ice. 'You will see. We shall find you a Greek husband in no time at all.'

'I doubt that Lorna wishes for anything as permanent as a husband.' Jason materialised out of the shadows. 'That would cramp your style, would it not?' he asked her.

'That would depend entirely on the husband,' Lorna said. 'If one was married to a monster I suppose it would.'

'Ah! But I am sure you are far too ... too astute ... to fall in love ... much less marry such a man.' He bared his teeth in a smile totally lacking in warmth.

'I didn't know astu ... er ... *astuteness* ... had anything to do with falling in love,' she replied with a faint hiccup.

'It does for *some* women,' he said bitterly.

Lorna's partner came back at that moment, and when he handed her her glass of champagne she made a point of fluttering her eyelashes at him, and took grim satisfaction from seeing Jason's face cloud. Defiantly she downed her wine and was led on to the dance floor again, for the band had started to play.

By the time supper was served she was feeling rather dizzy, and she refused the various wines that accompanied the meal. In spite of this precaution the stars swung crazily in the sky whenever she ventured to tilt her head and look at them.

When the plates had been cleared away and the tables moved back, the Cretan dances began. Soon a line of male dancers, led by Jason, was winding its way around the deck. This was a very different dance from the one he had performed for her at the café. This was a dance of pure pride. The dancers, hands joined, wove the complicated steps, handed down from generation to generation, and the rhythms of their flying feet beat out a tattoo of exultation at being Cretan.

Lorna's champagne-induced high spirits started to fade, for nothing could have underlined more clearly the gulf that separated her from Jason. Suddenly she felt foreign. Alien. And very lonely. Unobtrusively she moved her chair back into the shadows, as if to stress her sense of isolation.

The dancing came to an end and the disco band returned. Lorna's Athenian admirers flocked around her again and begged for dances. She drifted round the deck in the arms of one or the other, but all zest had gone from the evening. She drank another glass of champagne in an effort to recapture it but it merely made her feel muzzy, and when Ariadne came searching for her to say they must leave, she felt relief. This quickly vanished when she discovered that Jason was driving them home.

'Mama left with the limousine after supper,' Ariadne explained, 'she did not wish to spoil our pleasure by saying good night, and breaking up the party.'

Jason joined the two girls. '*Ela*, Ariadne! It grows late,' he said. He ignored Lorna.

Lorna bade good night to her host and made her way—very carefully—down the gangplank, followed by Jason. His sister stayed on deck a moment longer to have a brief goodbye with her fiancé.

Jason looked very forbidding. 'Do you know why Nikos did not come to the party?' he asked her.

She was tempted to tell him the truth. That she had not even missed Nikos. Had not even noticed that he wasn't there, but she merely said, 'I've no idea what happened to him.'

'It was most discourteous. And insulting to Kosti and his guests. My cousin's manners leave much to be desired.' She had the feeling that he was reprimanding her, too. Identifying her with Nikos because he thought they were lovers.

Ariadne ran down the gangplank, her yellow skirt billowing, and the three of them piled into the white Mercedes. Ariadne in the front with her brother; Lorna at the back.

During the drive, while Ariadne prattled on about the party and Jason drove with tight-lipped efficiency, Lorna started to become angry. Angry with Jason and his impossible behaviour. Just who did he think he was? Punishing her like this with his icy silence. Why! he hadn't even asked her for *one* dance. He had no reason to sulk at all, she told herself. *She* should be the one to be offended—he'd ignored her all evening. And he had the *gall* to lecture her about discourtesy. He was a fine one to talk! She managed to work herself into a thorough temper and in order to let off steam started singing softly . . . 'I could have danced all night. I could have danced all night . . .' through clenched teeth.

Jason parked in front of the villa and opened the door for his sister. When he went round to help Lorna she ignored his hand and climbed out of the car unaided.

Ariadne kissed her brother good night. '*Kalinihta*, Jason . . . It was a lovely party was it not?'

'Lovely, *kookla mou*.' He kissed her forehead tenderly. 'And you graced it well. Kosti is a very lucky man. Now go to bed. It is late.' When she had gone into the dark house he turned to Lorna and said formally, '*Kalinihta*. I trust you will sleep well.'

'I'm not in the least sleepy,' her stubborn chin jutted. 'I could dance and dance for hours.'

'So I gathered from your serenade. Can I offer you anything? Some lemonade . . .?'

'Nothing thank you. I think I'll just take a turn around the garden . . . get some air . . . good night.'

'I will accompany you,' he said. 'Unless you wish to be alone for any reason.' He looked at her with mistrust, and Lorna knew very well he suspected she had arranged to meet Nikos. This added more fuel to her already smouldering temper.

'Please yourself!' She started humming defiantly again and went down towards the garden with Jason following.

The swimming pool was smooth as a saucer of milk in the moonlight. When she reached the flagstoned edge she lifted her arms and started to dance, spinning around in wider and wider circles.

Jason came up to her. 'You dance very well, Lorna, but I think . . .'

'How can you tell whether I dance well or not?' She stopped for a moment to glare at him. 'You've never danced with me.'

'You seemed to be on the dance floor all evening,' he said, 'I could not get near you.'

'I had a very good time. I love to dance.' To illustrate this she started waltzing again, twirling around the edge of the pool.

'However, Lorna, I think . . .'

She interrupted him, holding her arms out at shoulder height. 'You're not the only one who can dance solo you know.' She was aware that she was being childish, but temper and champagne goaded her.

'I merely want to wa . . .'

'I'm going to dance till *dawn*!' She executed a whirling hop, stumbled over her feet, and fell headlong into the deep end of the pool.

She surfaced, spluttering and gasping. Jason knelt at the edge. He looked as if he was about to jump in and rescue her. 'Are you all right, Lorna?'

'Fine!' she giggled, 'A dip was just what I needed.' She turned on to her back and floated, her long chiffon skirt undulating round her like sea-weed. 'The water's lovely,' she informed him.

'I did try to warn you,' he said.

'Yes.' She paddled closer to the edge and confided, 'I think I may have had a little too much champgne.'

'Ah!' He suppressed a smile. 'Then a swim should be very beneficial.' He stood again and watched her as she swam slowly down the length of the pool to the shallow end. 'I notice your immersion has restored your temper,' he remarked as she started to climb out.

'I was silly,' she admitted, 'but you can be very irritating you know.' She kicked off her sodden sandals which squelched with every step and walked towards him. Her hair was a sleek cap on her head, her gown streamed water. When she approached she heard his intake of breath, and noticed his hands clench. He was staring at her hungrily, and she thought she saw him tremble.

She faltered and looked down at her dress, then she gasped in dismay. She looked like a naked river-nymph clad only in turquoise moonbeams, for the water had made the filmy material almost transparent, so that it clung to her body revealingly. She held her hands across her breasts in an attempt to cover herself, but he reached out and pulled them away.

'*Mou theos!* Lorna.' His voice was husky. 'You drive me mad.' He pulled her roughly into his arms and brought his mouth down on hers. His lips felt warm. Demanding, passionate.

She sighed in surrender and clung to him, all caution forgotten. She burned with joy at the touch of his mouth and her lips parted under his willingly. His steel-strong arms held her tightly, and she could feel the hardness of his body against hers. She slid her hand under his jacket and started to unbutton his shirt, which was wet now from her dress. His breathing· grew harsher as she stroked his chest, tangling her fingers in the dark hair.

With an inarticulate cry he passed his hands firmly down her body, moulding and cupping her breasts with skilful fingers. Her nipples grew hard under their flimsy covering of wet chiffon, and she arched against him in voluptuous delight. She was unaware of anything in the world now except her blinding need for him. He pulled away from her with a shuddering sigh, and gazed at her with flint-green eyes. She stood, unashamed, waiting for him to take her, here in the garden. Or to lead her to his room.

'*Ochi*,' he whispered softly, 'no.' He was very pale in the first flush of dawn, his hair tangled in a dark mass over his forehead, his shirt unbuttoned to his waist. He bent to retrieve his tie which had fallen at their feet. When he faced her again his expression was blank.

She stood mutely, a draped statue, while shame flowed over her in a burning tide. She did not move when he took off his white dinner jacket and put it over her shoulders.

'It would not be right, Lorna.' His voice sounded flat. 'In spite of your opinion of me I do not make love to another man's woman. Not even when she is as . . . as beautiful . . . as you.'

She had the sickening feeling he was going to say . . . 'as willing as you,' but had thought better of it. What little pride she had left stopped her from protesting that she belonged to no one. That she wanted only to belong to him.

'Come Lorna . . . *ela* . . . it is late.' He went to put his arm round her shoulders but she eluded him. If he touched her now she was afraid that she might weep, and picking up her ruined sandals she silently followed him into the sleeping villa.

CHAPTER SIX

THE next day was horrible. Lorna woke at noon feeling depressed and with a bad headache. She lay in bed watching the bright pencils of sunlight poke through the slats of the blind and wondered how she would ever find the courage to get up and go downstairs, where she would inevitably meet Jason. Humiliation covered her like one of the bed-sheets, and nasty phrases like ... 'pushover' and 'easy lay' kept clanging away in her aching head.

After about an hour of this futile wallowing she forced herself to shower and dress and then with a feeling of impending doom she crept out on to the upstairs landing.

The house was silent. It was the siesta hour. With luck she could probably slip away without meeting a soul. She tiptoed down the stairs to the front door. Outside the landscape quivered with heat. The sun hit her like a fist, and she blinked involuntarily in the merciless light.

'Ah! Lorna. There you are!' Blinded by the glare she had not seen Madam Peritakis, who was seated in a corner of the patio under a large striped sun-umbrella, a low table holding a tray with glasses and cups and saucers in front of her. 'Here is orange-juice and coffee,' she said, 'will you join me?'

Lorna couldn't think of anything she wanted more than a long cold glass of juice at that moment, so she thankfully seated herself in the blessed shade beside her hostess.

'Jason and Ariadne have deserted us,' Madam Peritakis said. 'They have gone to join Kosti for swimming.' She handed Lorna an ice-cold glass of juice.

'We decided not to wake you. We felt you needed sleep more than a swim. I hope we did right?'

A self-betraying flush swept Lorna's face. Oh God! did Madam Peritakis know about last night's escapade? She wasn't sure where Jason's mother slept. Maybe her bedroom was facing the pool and she had heard . . . and seen, all that had happened. Overcome with guilt Lorna mumbled something inaudible and sipped her juice.

'Was it not a most successful party?' Madam Peritakis asked. Without waiting for an answer she went on, 'I think a party on board ship is one of the nicest kind. Do you not agree?'

'I . . . I guess so. I mean . . . I've never been to a party on a yacht before.' She knew this sounded clumsy, but she wasn't up to being tactful. She was too tired and miserable. Besides the sooner the entire Peritakis family realised she came from a different kind of world from theirs the better it would be.

'I did not have a chance to thank you properly for your kindness to Ariadne last night,' her hostess now said. Lorna looked at her blankly. 'Helping her with her orchids. I know it was not the tragedy Ariadne felt it to be, but she is naturally very highly strung these days. She . . . how do you say it? She . . . *emphasises* things.'

'*Exaggerates*,' Lorna suggested, putting her empty glass back on the tray.

'Ah! My English! Exaggerates . . . of course.'

'It was nothing,' Lorna assured her. Madam Peritakis indicated the coffee-pot and she carefully nodded her head. 'Yes, please. It was just lucky I happened to remember that trick with the wire.'

'Nevertheless it was kind of you to take the time to assist a young girl. Not everyone would have bothered. Carol, for instance, would not.'

'Carol?' Lorna looked at Madam Peritakis vacantly, wondering if it was her headache that was making her particularly dull, for she hadn't the faintest idea who they were talking about.

'Ariadne has not told you of Carol?'

'No, she hasn't.'

'Carol was an American girl who visited our village four years ago.' She placed a cup of coffee before her guest. 'We got to know her and she spent much time with us. She was a beautiful girl . . . very sophisticated. She and Jason were attracted to each other and I . . . thought . . . they would get married.'

The scalding coffee did not hurt Lorna as much as the stab of jealousy that seared through her. 'What happened?' she asked when she'd recovered her breath.

'I am not sure. But I gather Carol felt she was too . . . too worldly . . . for a life in Crete.'

Lorna forced herself to speak in a neutral tone. 'In a way I can understand that,' she said, 'after all there are enormous cultural differences. She . . . Carol . . . must have felt awfully lonely sometimes.'

'Carol never felt lonely in her life.' The older woman bit her lip with vexation. 'I did not like her,' she said at last, 'she was cold.'

'But Jason liked her,' Lorna said, looking down into the dregs of her coffee to hide the pain in her wide eyes.

'Ah! Jason is a man!' His mother waved her hands expressively. 'She was beautiful and amusing . . . he was bored. And he knows it is time he was married. None of the Greek girls I have introduced him to have attracted him,' she added wistfully.

Since his mother was in this confiding mood Lorna figured she might as well find out all she could. It might help to cure her need for him. And if it was painful— well so was an operation. 'I suppose you'd prefer him to marry . . . one of his own kind?' she said.

Madam Peritakis looked surprised. 'Of course I would not! I want him to be happy. That was why I was prepared to accept Carol. And I know my children. Jason will never be happy with a compliant wife. He needs a woman who is not afraid to stand up to him. Then he will respect her.'

'Just the same,' Lorna persisted, 'with two such different backgrounds, I guess he and ... and Carol ... never had a chance.'

'Their backgrounds had nothing to do with it.' She sounded quite put out. 'Carol wanted to change my son. To make him into another person. That will never work. That she lost him was entirely her own fault. It had nothing to do with her background.'

But Lorna was stubborn. 'It puts a strain on a relationship though, doesn't it?' she said. 'When you're both used to such different ways of life.'

'Do you really believe that?' Madam Peritakis regarded her young companion thoughtfully before saying, 'I believe that when there is a deep and abiding love between two people these "differences" melt away like the snow on the mountains in spring.'

'I wonder.' Lorna looked out over the bleached valley that shimmered in the afternoon sun. 'I wonder if it's that simple.'

'I did not say it was *simple*,' Jason's mother replied firmly, 'oh no my dear! Quite the reverse. It takes patience and respect for each other. Is it not the same for you in your work?'

'That's true,' Lorna agreed. 'It's not quite as easy as it looks to the uninitiated.'

Madam Peritakis smiled kindly. 'You see, my dear. In your heart you agree with me after all.'

Lorna decided this conversation was becoming dangerous. 'While we're on the subject of photography, Madam Peritakis,' she said, in an effort to change the topic, 'I was wondering if I might be allowed to take some photographs of Ariadne's wedding? Informal ones of her going to the church, and afterwards at the reception. I promise to be unobtrusive.' She'd had this at the back of her mind for some time, and this seemed a good time to broach the subject. She planned to buy a handsome album, mount her pictures in it, and give it to the bride and groom for a surprise present. Madam

Peritakis seemed pleased with the idea and permission was granted.

When the older woman had retired for a nap Lorna put on her sun-hat and slinging her camera round her neck went in search of interesting shots for her portfolio. Work seemed the only escape from the painful memory of Jason's rejection. Not that she could forget it completely, but at least when she forced herself to concentrate on light and composition, and the myriad pitfalls between the idea and the finished result the pain in her heart was dulled a little. Work did help, and she decided to bury herself in it. Like taking aspirin for her headache.

She ignored the road today and instead went down towards the orange groves, following a track beside the river. Although it was now mid-afternoon it was still very hot, and the sound of the shallow river as it flowed swiftly down between rocks was refreshing.

At one point the stream fell over a small incline and a natural pool had been created where the water was a marvellous shade of green, like shimmering jade in the limestone basin. When she had taken several shots of this spot she sat down and trailed her hand in the transparent water. Within seconds her hand was cramped with cold, for only a short time before this water had been snow melting on the heights above her, running underground in places deep in the heart of the numinous mountains before it bubbled out into the sunlit world below.

She lay on her stomach and looked at the restless flow of sparkling crystal. The ground felt warm through her thin cotton skirt, as if it radiated the stored heat of a thousand summers.

What had Madam Peritakis said? That differences between people who loved each other melted like the snow on the mountains. Well it hadn't melted for Carol and Jason. Something had happened between those two that had scarred him, and now he mistrusted all North

American women. Particularly those with careers . . .
particularly Lorna.

Of course, she thought, there's no love between us,
only lust. The way she'd behaved, clinging to him so
ardently, willing him to possess her, surely that was lust
of the most powerful and overwhelming kind. But even
as she thought that she knew that it was not true. At
least it wasn't true for her. She had never felt this way
before. Had never known such hunger, so that she felt
she would die without him. And not just hunger for his
body, but for all of him. His friendship, his good
opinion, even for his country. She sat upright, 'Oh my
God!' she said aloud, 'I'm in love with him.'

Her first reaction to this astounding insight was pure
blazing joy. She sat quite still. She could hear the faint
metallic clanking of goat bells and somewhere far away
a shepherd played a sad little tune on a flute. The thin
sounds drifted through the air like filaments of silk. She
hugged herself and said again slowly . . . 'I love Jason'
. . . savouring the words like wine.

Gradually her elation faded. She might . . . did . . .
love him. But nothing could change the fact that he had
refused her when she had offered herself to him. Hardly
the action of a man in love, or even attracted to a
woman. And he thought she was Nikos's mistress. Why
on earth hadn't she denied that right from the start?
Pride, that's why, she thought, and blindness. And
stupid, *stupid* pride.

But that could be fixed. She would explain it to him.
Tell him it was all a silly misunderstanding, and . . . and
then what? Have him rebuff her again. She didn't think
she could stand that.

Slowly she got to her feet and started walking
towards the village. Far from feeling joy, now her
depression had deepened, for there was nothing she
could do. Except forget him. And that she knew now
was impossible.

Grin and bear it then. She had no other choice. Keep

this love hidden away in the depths of her heart, like that underground river. A private grief that would dull with time but never disappear. And work hard. Go on climbing up her professional ladder, knowing that no matter how brilliantly she succeeded there would always be an emptiness at the core of her life which would leave her unfulfilled forever.

Outwardly she would be the same Lorna McCann. Cheerful and competent. What she felt inside was nobody's business but her own. Her pride would help her save face.

By now she had reached the outskirts of the village. Here stood the small whitewashed church where Ariadne would be married next Saturday. Lorna leaned on the stone wall and looked at the worn gravestones. A woman and a little girl were tidying one of the graves, talking softly together. The noise of their trowel grated on the stony earth. Beside the church was a field with a patch of scarlet poppies that Lorna had noticed before and meant to photograph. Now she unslung her camera and walked around the churchyard to get to the flowers. She'd never seen such huge poppies before. After taking a couple of shots of the field she knelt down to take several close-ups of individual blooms. They were like crumpled silk, their centres marked with a wide black cross.

When she'd finished she became aware that she had an audience. The little girl who had been working in the graveyard was now standing behind her. She smiled shyly, pointed to the flowers and said something in Greek. Taking out her phrase book Lorna looked up the phrase for 'very beautiful' and tried it out. The child giggled and started chattering away at a great rate, her dark eyes sparkling.

'Hey! Steady on,' Lorna laughed, 'slowly ... *siga* ... I don't understand Greek.'

Shrugging her shoulders the child pointed to the poppies, then mimed taking a photograph. She seemed to find the idea of anyone taking a picture of a flower very amusing.

Lorna nodded her head. 'Yes,' she said, 'I take photos. Would you like me to take one of you?' She pulled her polaroid camera out of her canvas bag, and moving the little girl into a good light focused and pushed the shutter release. When the print emerged from the camera the child watched in fascination. 'Now we must wait a minute,' Lorna said. She tore the print off and waved it around, then showed it as the image started to come through. Gradually the colours grew sharper, and when the picture was finally ready she handed it to the girl. 'For you,' she said, '*parakalo*.'

The child's face lit up when she understood that she was to keep the picture. She breathlessly thanked Lorna ... ''*Feristo* ... '*feristo*,' and went racing back to the churchyard calling, 'Mamma, mamma!' at the top of her voice, waving her picture like a banner.

Lorna had just replaced the camera and was about to go on when she was hailed by the child's mother. '*Ella* ... Missus ... *ella parakalo*.'

For a moment Lorna wondered if she'd committed some awful gaffe by taking a photograph of the woman's daughter, but as she approached she was relieved to see that the mother was smiling. She held up the picture and gestured to it.

'Is beautiful ... *efharisto* ... come please ... *ella*!' She gestured to a tiny house that stood farther down towards the village. Smiling and nodding Lorna went with them. The woman kept up a constant flow of Greek, interspersed with the odd English phrase, most of which Lorna found incomprehensible, but it didn't seem to matter, and by the time they reached the chin-high wall of the house she felt she was with old friends.

Her hostess opened the rickety wooden gate. Beyond was a minute courtyard, scrupulously swept, with a stack of vine clippings for firewood. There was a stone sink out here too, with a channel cut for the water to run away. Against one wall was an animal house with a donkey and a couple of chickens. A goat was tethered outside the wall. The Greek woman darted into the house and returned carrying a small straight-backed chair for her guest. She pointed to herself and said, 'Maria.' Pulled her little daughter to her side and pointed to her, 'Irene', then she pointed to Lorna. Lorna told her her name and after Maria had repeated it several times she went back into the house, returning in a few minutes with a battered tin tray which had a glass of water, a small spoon in a bowl of jam, and a cup of Turkish coffee on it.

Lorna had heard of this ancient and delightful symbol of Greek hospitality, but never before had she been offered 'spoon sweets'. She thanked her lucky stars she knew she was not expected to eat the entire bowl of jam, as some confused foreign visitors had been known to do. She took a spoonful of jam, ate it, drank the glass of water and put the spoon in the empty glass, then she drank the coffee. She knew now she was supposed to thank her hostess and wish her and her family good fortune. The fact that her Greek only ran to the first part of this custom plainly didn't bother Maria who smiled broadly at her attempts to speak her language.

'I ... learn you ... Greek,' she said while Lorna struggled with her phrase book. She set about this task immediately, taking a stick and scratching out the Greek alphabet in the dust at their feet. Dutifully Lorna copied it into her notebook. She repeated words after Maria and Irene—who thought the whole lesson exquisitely funny—and after a while she managed to comprehend the fact that Maria was a widow, and that it was her husband's grave she had been tending when Lorna met them. She also figured out that Irene was seven years old and was an only child.

Just before the lesson came to an end Maria pointed to the village and laying her cheek on her hands and closing her eyes asked, 'Taverna?'

'No ... *ochi* ... Peritakis villa,' Lorna replied, pointing up the mountainside.

Maria's mobile face lit up and she kissed her fingers. 'Ah! Peritakis ... *kalo* ... good ... Jason Peritakis good man ... *dombros*.'

She was unmistakably enthusiastic about Jason, and Lorna warmed to her even more. Knowing she was safe to show something of her true feelings here she nodded vigorously and said, 'Jason ... yes he is very *kalo* ... very good. I agree.' It made her happy just to say his name aloud, and she felt that by learning to speak his language she would somehow bind herself to him. She would look forward to coming to this humble little house, and maybe once or twice during the lesson she would casually mention him and bask in the glow of Maria's visible admiration. It wasn't a lot, but it was better than nothing.

By the time she left her two new friends the sky was layered with a mauve-and-purple sunset and she was beginning to feel very hungry.

She arrived at the taverna to find it buzzing with activity. The new group from Athens had arrived and the place was bursting at the seams. Savoury smells were coming from the spit where a long spiced sausage called a *kokoretsi* revolved over the charcoal. Pots of different stew and vegetables simmered on the open kitchen stove, and plates of Greek salad stood on the glassed-in refrigerated counter.

Vasily, busily fussing over the garden lights, waved a welcome. 'Miss Susan is up in the stairs,' he informed Lorna. 'You go to her.'

Lorna gave him a bright smile—even though she wasn't feeling particularly happy—and made her way up to the bedroom she had shared with her friend—was it only a couple of weeks ago? It felt like years.

When she knocked on the door Susan flung it open and pulled her inside. 'Lorna! Great! I was hoping you'd be by this evening. I want your advice about all this.' She waved towards her bed which was piled with clothes.

Lorna shut the door behind her. 'What are you doing "Susie Q"? Having a rummage sale?'

'I'm having a good old clear-out,' Susan beamed. 'I've decided that everything I own ... except the dress you gave me ... is the "pits". So I'm going to dump the lot.' She looked at Lorna, her brown eyes sparkling. Lorna had never seen her look so pretty.

Lorna picked up a plain cotton shirt from the heap of clothes on the bed. 'Steady on, Susie! Don't go mad. This is perfectly okay for heaven's sake! And why the sudden need for an haute-couture wardrobe? You don't need it for the dig surely?'

'Well ... in the evenings after work. And for dates,' she blushed scarlet.

'Dates indeed!' Lorna teased. 'What have you been up to since I moved out? Out with it, Susie. Tell your Auntie Lorna.'

Susan sat down on the bed, dislodging several pairs of violently coloured polyester slacks that slithered on to the floor. 'Oh! Lorna,' she said, her rosy face serious now, 'his name is Harvey. He's the new supervisor ... with that lot from Athens. He's from Ohio ... and his speciality is ceramics, just like mine ... and ... oh! he's terrific ... and he thinks I am too ... terrific I mean.' She bounced off the bed and grabbed Lorna's hands. 'We have so much in common. But it's more than that. I feel so happy ... I could *sing*! It's never happened to me before ... don't laugh.' She peered anxiously at her friend.

'Laugh? Susan, honey, I think it's wonderful,' Lorna said gently. 'Bless you. Now let's sort out these clothes of yours. Come on! Being in love doesn't excuse you from helping.' She began to methodically go through the mound of clothes, dropping the discarded garments on to the floor, half-hearing Susan as she chattered on about Harvey. About how handsome he was ... and how clever ... and how the first night he'd arrived they'd sat and talked about the Minoans and their mysterious disappearance from Crete thirty-four centuries ago. And how they hadn't stopped talking till dawn, so enthralled were they with each other's company. And Lorna smiled and nodded and sorted clothes, while her heart ached so much she thought it would break.

She was genuinely happy for her friend, but she couldn't help feeling that the timing was unfortunate, for on her way to the taverna she had decided to tell Susan all about her muddle with Jason. Admit that she was in love with him, and probably allow herself the luxury of a good cry. Now she felt that she couldn't do this. She couldn't impose her unhappiness on her friend. It would be too selfish. Susan was a generous-hearted girl, and Lorna knew she would be more than willing to lend a sympathetic ear to her troubles. But she was afraid it would take some of the pleasure out of the older girl's evening, and she didn't want to do that. Meanwhile, Susan blithely talked about her new-found love, unaware that with every word she was making her friend feel sadder and sadder.

Later they joined the others for dinner and Lorna was introduced to Harvey. He was a pleasant young man, plump and kindly. Lorna liked him right away, and was pleased to see that he was clearly crazy about Susan. He sat between the two girls at the long table under the plane tree, and was courteous enough to divide his attention between them, although anyone with a half a brain could tell that Susan was really the only person he was aware of.

'I understand you've moved on to grander things these days,' he said, referring to Lorna's move to the villa.

'Pretty grand,' she agreed, then added, 'but it's really only a dormitory arrangement. And to be handy for my dark-room.'

'And how's dreamy Jason?' Susan asked, helping herself to salad. 'Jason Peritakis is sort of Lorna's landlord,' she explained to Harvey. 'He's very charming, and *I* think he's sweet on her. She doesn't think so, though.'

Neither would you if you knew the way he rejected me last night, Lorna thought, but she merely said, 'I don't know how he is. I hardly ever see him. We live at different levels.' And the subject was dropped.

It was a relaxed evening with a lot of cheerful banter being tossed around the table. The extra fieldworkers had come at just the right pyschological moment and this noisy dinner was quite like old times, before the theft of the seal stones had put a pall of gloom over everything.

On the surface Lorna seemed as high-spirited as the rest of the group, and no one would have guessed the effort it cost her to laugh and joke with her colleagues. But when one of the supervisors, who rented a house further up the mountain, offered her a lift in his car she accepted with alacrity.

It was still fairly early when she arrived at the villa. Lights were burning in the sitting room, and with a beating heart she poked her head round the door to say good night. Only Madam Peritakis was there, seated in an armchair, a book open on her lap.

'The others dined in Iraklion tonight,' she told Lorna, 'Ariadne phoned to invite you to join them, but you were nowhere to be found.'

'That was nice of her,' Lorna said, thanking providence she had left for her walk when the call came. 'But I really think an early night is what I need.'

Madam Peritakis nodded, then she asked casually, 'Tell me, do you happen to know where Nikos is? He was supposed to dine with me tonight, but he did not come, and when I telephoned his house there was no reply. I wondered if perhaps you might have seen him at the taverna.'

'I haven't seen him since we finished work on Friday.'

'No matter. Doubtless he forgot.' She gave Lorna a rueful smile. 'Nikos is a troubled soul,' she said. 'His own . . . how is it? Worst enemy.'

'Yes. I gathered that.'

'It is sad.' Abruptly she changed the subject. 'You look tired, child,' she said, 'I must not keep you from your bed. Sleep well.'

As Lorna climbed the stairs to her room she wondered idly what could have happened to Nikos. First missing the party, then dinner with his aunt. She thought it quite possible that he never had any intention of keeping either date, but just didn't have the nerve to refuse. But where he might be really didn't interest her. What occupied her thoughts while she prepared for bed was wondering if Ariadne's invitation to dinner had been prompted by her brother. Somehow Lorna doubted that. It seemed far more likely he would want to stay as far away from her as possible. To him she was just another North American girl in search of adventure. A boring nuisance.

She climbed wearily into bed, her own feelings in a turmoil. She dreaded seeing him again. Yet the thought of not seeing him at all was too awful to contemplate. She had no idea what she would say when she *did* see him, and she swung between violent changes of emotion; one minute longing to dash out and greet his car when she heard it pull up in the drive, the next wondering if she could make other living arrangements so as not to be an embarrassment to him and to herself. But in the midst of these tangled emotions one thing came through loud and clear. Despite any differences in background the love she felt for Jason was unshakeable, and so intense it frightened her.

She woke at dawn to the sound of horses' hooves, and leaping out of bed peeped round the silk curtains. Jason's raven head gleamed in the early sunlight as he led his horse to the edge of the garden. Then he mounted and digging his heels into his mount's sides galloped off down the track beside the river.

Hastily she showered and dressed in old shorts and shirt. If she hurried she could be on her way to the site before he came back, for with the morning she felt she needed more time to pass before she faced him again. As it was just seeing the back of his head had set her pulses racing. She doubted she would be capable of speech if she met him face to face.

As quietly as she could she took her cameras and film from the dark-room, then ran hard through the orange groves down to the meadows below. It was so early that mist still wrapped the valley, making the distorted trunks of olive trees look like strange figures from another world. An old man, taking advantage of the early morning coolness to work on his *kipos* hailed her. '*Yia sas!*'

She waved back and dared a short Greek phrase. '*Ti kanete?*' . . . How are you?'

A grin wreathed his weather-beaten face. '*Kala efharisto.*' He nodded approval of her attempt at Greek. 'Bravo! Bravo!'

Slowing down to a walk she waved goodbye and headed for the taverna. She would have plenty of time for some breakfast before work. She willed herself not to look back in the direction of the villa to see if Jason was returning from his early ride.

Vasily was mopping the floor of the indoor dining room when she arrived. He greeted her warmly and leaning his mop against the wall headed for the kitchen.

'Ah! Miss Lorna you are the early owl this morning.'

'I think you mean "early bird",' Lorna smiled.

Unimpressed he shrugged. 'Owl is bird . . . no?' He put bread, butter, and marmalade on to a small tray, then busied himself with the coffee. 'But you are not the first to eat the fast . . . no. See . . . in the garden.' He nodded through the open door towards the plane tree, his usually good-natured face grim.

Seated in solitary state was Nikos, a steaming pot of coffee before him. He looked distinctly the worse for wear.

Lorna's heart sank, and she realised that for a wild moment she had hoped it would be Jason sitting there, waiting for her.

'You wish to join him?' Vasily asked. 'Or would you better eat alone? I finish on the floor soon.'

'No. I'll join him.' She took the tray, 'I'll take this. You go on with your work,' and over his protests she carried her breakfast into the garden.

Nikos raised a bleary eye. 'Lorna! How nice,' his good-looking, dissipated face brightened. 'So you do not eat with the rich ones. You remember your humble friends.'

'You'd better be very humble indeed,' Lorna said, 'I think you've got a fair bit of explaining to do up at the villa.' He looked at her glassily. 'About your disappearing act. Weren't you supposed to go to the party on Saturday night?'

'Bah!' He lifted his coffee cup with both hands to keep it steady. 'I had much business on Saturday. I could not waste time with silly parties.'

'It's nothing to do with me,' Lorna said, 'I just thought I'd warn you, that's all.' Privately she thought that whatever business he may have had it certainly included drinking. He reeked of stale wine fumes.

Nikos fumbled in his jacket and brought out a wallet which he waved under Lorna's nose. It was bursting with drachma bank notes. 'See, Lorna! I now have money ... and the chance to make much more. No longer is Jason the clever one, I too am clever.' Unsteadily he replaced the wallet, and Lorna realised he was still a little drunk.

Diplomatically she tried to change the subject. 'I thought I was early this morning, Nikos,' she said chattily, 'but you've beaten me to it. You must be really keen to get to work.'

'I have just come from Rethimnon ... on the first bus. I have not been to my house at all.'

That explained his unshaven face. 'That's a long way off, isn't it?' she said. For the little town of Rethimnon was about sixty miles west of Iraklion.

'It was where my business took me,' he said portentously, then suddenly he became cautious. 'But do not tell anyone, Lorna. Do not tell Jason.'

'Jason and I don't exchange confidences,' she said bitterly.

'That is good,' he looked at her slyly, 'he is a hard man. With no kindness in him.'

'I don't happen to agree with you,' she said, pushing back her chair and rising. 'And I make it a rule not to discuss people behind their backs. I'm going up to the site now. See you later.'

All day she tried to find the hardest jobs she could. She thought if she could exhaust herself physically she might deaden the pain she felt whenever she thought of Jason ... which was all the time! She took photographs from every difficult angle she could find. Then she got herself assigned on a team that was breaking ground in one of the 'grids'. She hauled buckets of earth and emptied them into a wheelbarrow, which she then wheeled away and dumped on a tarpaulin sheet where another member of the team sifted and searched for shards or other small finds.

By noon her back and arms were aching and her hair was sticking to her head under her old sun-hat. Rivulets of sweat coursed down her dusty face. When the lunch break came she sank thankfully down under an olive tree. She was joined by Susan and Harvey, and to her annoyance by Nikos, who brought out a bottle of wine from his bag. A practice discouraged by Professor Spanakis, who wasn't keen about drinking on the job. When the others had refused his offer of a drink he took a long pull from the bottle and leaned moodily against the gnarled trunk.

'I'd go easy on that stuff if I were you,' Harvey told him, 'we've got a lot of work to do this afternoon remember.'

'Ah! Spanakis makes us work like the *mules*!' Nikos said. 'Like peasants. *Worse* than peasants.'

Susan glared at him. 'If you don't like the work you can always quit,' she said. Now that Harvey had come into her life she found it easier to stand up to Nikos. He no longer intimidated her.

'It suits my purpose to work here for the moment. I ... I need to be here,' Nikos replied. 'Not for the miserable pittance we are paid, believe me. I do not need that. I have money now.' He smiled mysteriously and took another swig of wine.

Pulling her hat over her face Lorna lay back on the rough grass and tried to shut him out of her consciousness. He was like an annoying mosquito at a picnic. Besides, she had far too much to occupy her to bother about Nikos and his oblique references to money. The sun beat down like a hammer, so that even the insects were silenced. But here under the thick foliage of the olive tree it was cooler and gradually she drifted off to sleep.

She was awakened by a prod in the ribs from Susan who was introducing Harvey to someone who had just come up to the group. Lorna shifted crossly and opened her eyes. From under the brim of her hat she could see a pair of highly polished black leather boots. Her heart started to race painfully. She pushed her hat up another inch and looked into a pair of brilliant green eyes as Jason leaned down to shake Harvey's outstretched hand.

She wildly thought of pulling her hat back down over her face and feigning sleep, but realised he knew she was awake, and that such behaviour would be not only rude but childish. Slowly she pulled herself into a sitting position and pushed her hair out of her face. She kept her eyes down and stared at her feet, encased in grubby socks and hiking boots. Not the most glamorous footwear with shorts, but practical for shovelling earth.

Jason welcomed Harvey to the village. 'We have little to offer you in the way of entertainment,' he said, 'but the wine is good and the people are hospitable.'

'You're right there,' Harvey agreed scrambling to his feet, 'the people are great. And as for entertainment. I have all the entertainment I need just being part of this excavation. It's a real privilege being here Mr Peritakis.'

'The privilege is ours,' Jason said, and Lorna could hear the smile in his voice. 'And please to call me by my Christian name . . . all of you . . . let us not be formal.' He turned again to Havey. 'I recently read a paper of yours . . . about the eruption on Santorini . . . which I much enjoyed. I would be most happy if you could find the time to visit me one evening. To discuss your theories.'

Harvey stuttered with delight. 'Gee! . . . say, that'd be great . . .'

'It will have to be after my sister's wedding,' Jason continued. 'As Lorna has no doubt told you we are very busy with the preparations for this great day.'

It was the first time he had acknowledged her presence, and she stole a quick glance up at him through her thick lashes. His face was impassive, and when he caught her eye he looked away. No one would have guessed the flame of passion that had ignited them that early morning in the garden. But for Lorna the memory of his kiss stood firm between them, and she could not look at him without catching her breath. She carefully examined the toes of her boots again.

'But I must not interrupt your siesta any more,' Jason said. 'I came to have a few words with my cousin.' He addressed Nikos, who was still lounging against the trunk of the tree, his bottle of wine nearly empty now. 'Could I see you for a moment in private, Nikos? There is something I wish to discuss with you.'

Nikos said something in Greek, and it didn't require any knowledge of the language to know that he was objecting, but Jason firmly cut across his protestations, walked some distance away, then stood waiting for his cousin to join him.

Sullenly Nikos swallowed the last of his wine, then with a great show of nonchalance he walked over to Jason. They started to talk, softly at first, but gradually Nikos's voice rose to a blustering shout. Jason was evidently trying to calm him, but Nikos's face grew redder and redder and with a final bellow he returned to the three others and flung himself down beside Lorna, saying loudly, 'Did I not tell you, Lorna, always he insults me.' Morosely he tried to drain a few more drops from his empty wine bottle, then flung it away in irritation.

Lorna would have been happy if the sun-baked earth had opened up and swallowed her. From where Jason was standing he could not hear what Nikos had said, but it must have looked to him as if his cousin and Lorna were discussing that brief unpleasant scene like old buddies.

She looked over to Jason but he was too far away to see the mute appeal in her eyes. If she could have seen his expression clearly she might have been surprised, for it was anxiety rather than anger that etched his fine features. He stood irresolutely for a second, then turned and walked away. Every instinct urged her to get to her feet and follow him. Explain that the situation between herself and Nikos was not the way it must appear, that the charade had gone on too long. But fear, craven fear of another rejection from Jason, stopped her.

She waited until they saw him galloping away across the open hillside, then she excused herself and went to the storage hut, ostensibly for a drink of water, but really to be alone to lick her wounds, and to prepare a happy face for the rest of her working day.

CHAPTER SEVEN

LORNA decided to stay out of Jason's way, then she would avoid any more misunderstandings or unnecessary hurt. So each morning when she woke to the sound of his horse's hooves on the flagstoned path she would slip out of bed and hurriedly wash and dress. Flinging her cameras and film in her knapsack she would tear off across-country in time for breakfast at the taverna before Jason returned from his ride. After work she would race back to the villa to shower and change, then using the back stairs she would rush off again for her Greek lesson with Maria before dinner with her colleagues at Vasily's. By the time she came back to work in her dark-room the Peritakis family were usually out at some function or other connected with the coming wedding, and she would creep up to bed either before they were home, or when the lights had finally been turned off for the night. It was a tiring routine but it worked.

Jason did not come to the dig again. She told herself he was probably too busy. But she really believed he was staying away deliberately, and even though she was doing the same, the thought that he was shunning her depressed her.

Her lessons with Maria were fun though. They would sit at the table in the tiny kitchen facing a dresser hung with chipped crockery and a framed photograph of Maria's late husband. It was evident that Maria and her child lived in grinding poverty. Everything they owned—and they owned precious little—was threadbare, but scrupulously clean. The little table seemed to have a warp in it from incessant scrubbing, and the patterned edge on the stone floor had faded to a few indistinct lines from years of washing.

Maria, like all the village women, wore shabby black, a black kerchief tied over her head. Irene's two dresses were mended with such skill it was hard to see where the real material finished and the patch started, but her sandals were falling apart. To save them she went barefoot in the vicinity of the house. And she and her mother were very thin.

Lorna knew Maria would be deeply offended if she offered to pay for the lessons, so she had to content herself by bringing small presents for Irene. Presents for a child she knew were acceptable. She would bring chocolate bars and fruit. And sometimes she would buy cheese and olives, and the three of them would sit round the table sharing this meagre feast while Lorna struggled with a child's reader supplied by Irene.

Within a couple of days she found out that Maria had been a widow for three years. Her husband had been a shepherd and had died in an accident in the mountains. Her eyes filled whenever she talked of this, and always the Peritakis family was mentioned, and Lorna could sense, although she couldn't make out all the words, that they had been particularly supportive to Maria during that time. That she loved and admired them was without question. That she despised Nikos was equally clear. With the aid of Lorna's phrase book, Irene's reader, and a lot of eloquent hand gestures, she gathered that Nikos had always been unpopular and a trouble-maker, and that as far as Maria was concerned the sooner he left the village the happier everybody would be. 'He is not good . . . not *ombros*,' Maria said, and Lorna was inclined to agree.

Towards the end of the week, when she was exhausted from racing around in order to avoid the one person she actually longed to see, Susan approached her and suggested they take a half-day off to go shopping in Iraklion. She wanted to buy a dress for the wedding.

'I'm due some extra time,' said Susan, 'and as for you! You've been going full tilt all week. I'm sure old Spanakis won't begrudge you an afternoon.' Lorna was delighted to have a chance to break her hectic routine, so Professor Spanakis was approached and grudgingly gave his consent.

After lunch on the day of their planned expedition Lorna did her usual sprint back to the villa for a quick shower, and changed into a strapless apple-green sundress. She combed her wet, freshly washed hair into shape and applied a trace of lip gloss. She stared at her reflection for a moment. She was deeply tanned now, and her flesh looked like burnished satin against the crisp cotton of her dress, but a second glance revealed smudges of fatigue under her eyes. Her regime of relentless hard work was taking its toll. She dabbed a trace of pale make-up on the offending shadows to disguise them and impatiently flicked a wing of damp hair away from her cheek. It had grown longer, but because it had been expertly blunt-cut it had kept its shape and now swung bell-like well below her jaw line.

She picked up a white cotton beach-bag, thrust her wallet and the inevitable camera in it, and on impulse rammed her bikini and a towel in as well. If the shopping went well they might have time for a swim before catching the bus home.

She could hear voices behind the house when she stepped out on to the patio, so she decided to take the road down to the village rather than walk down the now familiar track through the orange groves.

Her sandals made no noise on the hot tarmac, and the sun poured over her in a beneficent flood, drying her hair to the colour of lustrous platinum. She was within sight of the village when Jason's white Mercedes shot round the curve, screeched to a stop, and reversed to where she was standing.

He leaned across the passenger seat. 'Lorna! What do you do here?'

It was the first time they had spoken since the morning after the party, when he had escorted her to her bedroom door. Her mouth was dry and she had difficulty answering casually. 'I'm on my way to the village ... to meet Susan,' she was astounded that she sounded quite normal for her blood was beating till it nearly deafened her.

'Not to go to the dig surely? Not in that dress.' His sea-green eyes flickered over her, taking in the sheen of her skin and her freshly shampooed hair.

'No. We're going to Iraklion for some shopping. We've got the afternoon off.'

'I too go to Iraklion. Come! I will drive you.' He opened the car door and waited for her to get in. Her first impulse was to refuse. To say coolly that she preferred to take the bus, but that seemed so crass she mumbled, 'Thank you,' instead and climbed into the car.

He did not drive off immediately but sat leaning back in his seat looking at her thoughtfully. He was wearing blue jeans this afternoon, not the scruffy variety they wore on the dig, but immaculate designer jeans that clung to his lean thighs, emphasising the hardness of his muscular legs. And his white T-shirt made his broad shoulders look more powerful than ever.

'It is fortunate that we meet like this,' he said, 'I have been wanting to speak alone with you for some time.'

'Oh?' There seemed to be a large stone lodged in her throat that made speech difficult.

'Have you been avoiding me, Lorna?' he asked.

'Well ... er ...' She dared to dart a glance at him, but when her blue eyes met his green ones she hastily looked down into her lap again and her glossy wings of hair slipped forward and covered her cheeks.

'Yes ... you have been avoiding me. It is because of the other night, *ne*? Because of what passed between us. I wanted to tell you ...' He paused and she finished for him.

'To forget it?'

He sat upright and gave her a long hard stare. 'Could you do that,' he said, 'could you forget it?'

Lorna tried to swallow the stone in her throat. 'No,' she whispered at last, 'I'm afraid I couldn't.'

'Afraid?' He leaned in closer towards her and she could smell the heady male fragrance of his skin. 'What is there to be afraid of?'

'Well . . . making a fool of myself, I suppose. No woman enjoys that.' She tried to sound light-hearted but failed dismally.

'You did not make a fool of yourself,' he said, 'the other night I wanted you, Lorna . . . and you wanted me. You will not deny that. You wanted me as much as I wanted you.'

Her face flamed and she was grateful for her obscuring curtain of hair. 'I don't deny it,' she said.

He reached out and gently turned her chin so that she was forced to look at him, then he stroked the line of her jaw with the tips of his fingers. She was unable to repress the shiver of pleasure his touch gave her. 'You wanted me,' he repeated.

There was a ring of self-satisfaction in this and it annoyed her. 'I'd had a lot of champagne,' she reminded him tartly.

The delicious stroking stopped. 'And that was the only reason?'

'Jason do we have to have this . . . this *post-mortem*?' She tried to turn her head away but he held her chin so tightly that she could not move.

'You are driving me *mad*!' he hissed. 'Whenever I try to find you, you are not there. You slip in and out of the house like a shadow . . . but I cannot forget you. You . . . you *haunt* me.' He glared at her accusingly. 'I must know if the other night was nothing more to you than . . . than too much champagne.' He released her chin and thrust his hand into the warm silk of her hair, tugging it back so that she was forced to look up at him. 'It was more than that, was it not, Lorna?'

He was so close she could see the texture of his skin, the close-shaven blue shadow of his beard. 'It was more than that,' she said softly. 'Much more.'

'Ah!' He loosed his grip on her hair but kept his hand on the nape of her neck. 'And what will you do, Lorna? About Nikos?'

'It has nothing to do with Nikos,' she said. 'Nothing at all.'

'Indeed!' His hand left her neck and fell on to the seatback. 'Is that not very . . . dishonest . . . not to tell your lover?'

'Sure it is. But Nikos doesn't happen to be my lover. He never has been.' Her mouth curved in a smile.

At that moment there was a blast from a loud klaxon horn that nearly sent her shooting through the sun-roof. Through the rear-view mirror they saw the bus for Iraklion just turning the bend, the driver blaring away on the horn to tell them they were blocking the narrow road.

With a curse Jason put the car into gear and shouting *'Endaxi! Endaxi!'* with Cretan zeal at the irate bus-driver he started down to the village.

Susan, who had been getting more and more anxious as the minutes ticked by, watched this cacophonous procession pull up at the bus-stop. Her round eyes grew rounder when her friend leaned out of the window of the gleaming car and called, 'Susan! Here! We're getting a lift. Don't get on the bus!'

'Lorna I must speak with you *alone*,' said Jason.

'Leave it to me.' Susan came up to them and Lorna said, 'Jason's going to drive us. Isn't that great? So we might have time for a swim in Iraklion, do you have your swim-suit with you?' Susan couldn't see Lorna's hands, or she would have noticed that her friends slim fingers were tightly crossed for luck.

'No. I didn't think . . .'

'Well why don't you get it, Susie? Jason doesn't mind

waiting. Do you Jason?' She darted a look at Jason who sat tensely at the wheel. 'And don't forget your sun-tan lotion and a towel.'

'Okay!' Susan started to trot towards the taverna.

'Don't hurry, Susie!' Lorna called after her. 'We've got loads of time.

'There!' she said triumphantly as Susan's plump figure disappeared, 'she'll be gone for *ages*. She always takes forever to find things.'

He turned off the engine and put his arm along the top of the seat. 'Is it true about Nikos?' he asked hoarsely. 'Is it true that he has never been your lover?'

'Quite true.' She felt as if a great weight had been lifted from her heart and she could breathe fully for the first time in days.

'But why did you never tell me?' he demanded.

'Because I was angry with you. Oh! I know it was dumb. But you just *assumed* we were lovers without any kind of evidence.'

'But that first night,' he protested, 'Nikos was so possessive. I thought . . .'

'I know you did. And I was so mad at you I let you go on thinking it.'

'And since then . . . and the other night . . .' His eyebrows drew together grimly. 'In spite of what had happened between us you still did not tell me.'

'I wanted to . . . but . . . it seemed the wrong time.' She coloured in spite of herself. 'I didn't want to tell you when we . . . when we both weren't thinking too clearly. You might have thought I was tricking you.'

'So you used this . . . this lie . . . to protect yourself from me. Is that right?' His gold-flecked eyes looked at her sadly.

'At the beginning . . . Yes.'

'And later?'

She twisted in her seat so that she faced him squarely. She wanted to *will* him to see into the depths of her heart. To see the truth there. 'I showed you how I feel when you made love to me by the pool. That wasn't a lie, Jason. I swear it.'

He looked at her for a long moment, then cupping her face in his hands he kissed her softly on the lips. His mouth felt warm on hers. '*Agapi mou*,' he said huskily, 'my love. My lovely, lovely Lorna.' He put his arms around her and held her tightly, kissing her eye-lids, her forehead, her hair. Time stood still for Lorna while she gave herself up to the voluptuous pleasure of his caresses.

There was a discreet cough and Susan's round face peered into the car. 'Er! I've got my swim-suit,' she said, 'are we still going to Iraklion?'

Lorna gave a yelp of laugher and buried her head in Jason's shoulder. '*Mou Theos*!' he exclaimed, 'the plane!'

Lorna giggled happily. 'What plane, darling?'

'The plane from Athens. I am to meet guests for the wedding tomorrow.' He slewed round and opened the rear door for Susan. 'For some reason that had completely slipped my mind,' he said with a smile that made Lorna's heart turn over.

Susan grinned. 'You don't say!' Settling back in the seat she added, 'It's nice you two have stopped barking at each other. And if I may so it was about time.'

'You may say so,' Jason said. 'And now, ladies, fasten your seat-belts while I overtake that bus.'

He drove fast and skilfully all the way to the city. But on every straight stretch of highway his hand caught and held Lorna's, and whenever his eyes met hers he gave her a look of such ardour she melted inside, and it seemed to her that the sun had never shone so brightly, nor the air felt so sweet.

Jason dropped the two women at a shopping area before going off to the airport. They arranged to meet him later at the beach.

Lorna's daze of happiness even extended to Iraklion, which she had never found to be an attractive town, since apart from its gigantic Venetian walls and harbour fortress it seemed to be built entirely of reinforced concrete. But this afternoon it glowed with charm, and the clamour that is one of the trademarks of the place sounded like a symphony to her ears.

She helped Susan choose a cream linen dress, and wavered between a white cotton dress embroidered with pink flowers, and a pink cotton dress embroidered with white flowers for Irene. Unable to make up her mind she bought them both. She also bought sandals for Irene, and hair-ribbons, and a large box of candy for Maria.

On their way to the beach Susan said, 'Aren't you going to buy anything for yourself, Lorna?'

Lorna held up her beach bag. 'I bought film ... remember?'

'That's for work, dummy. I mean something you want ... something pretty.'

They were walking by a row of jewellers' shops at that moment. Lorna stopped, looked in the window, and then went inside one of them. The shopkeeper greeted her in English but she tried out her Greek on him and he courteously switched to his own tongue. He brought out a tray of glass pendants shaped like blue eyes rimmed in silver. Lorna pored over the tray, her hair swinging forward in a flaxen curtain. 'I'll take this one,' she said in Greek, pointing to one of the smaller 'eyes', 'and a chain too, please.'

Susan, who had followed her friend into the shop, looked dubiously at the tray of garish charms. 'Are you sure you want that, Lorna? Look! There are some much cuter ones over there.' She pointed out some attractively carved ivory animals.

'Ur-hur!' Lorna shook her head vigorously. 'I want this. As a charm against the future.' She chose a slender silver chain and threaded the blue 'eye' on it, then fastened it round her neck. She paid the shopkeeper and they went back on to the street.

'What do you mean—charm against the future?' Susan demanded, hurrying to keep up with Lorna's long-legged stride.

'It's a charm to ward off the evil eye. My gesture of appeasement to the gods.'

'*Appeasement*. What are you talking about!' Susan's round face was turning pink with exertion.

Lorna stopped and put her hand on her friend's arm. 'I'm so happy "Susie Q". I don't want anything to go wrong . . . I couldn't bear it. So I've armoured myself against bad luck, that's all.' She fingered the bright piece of glass at her throat.

'You *nut*!' The older girl hugged her. 'Nothing's going to go wrong. He *adores* you. Don't be such an idiot.'

'But we're . . . different.'

'Of course you're different. He's a man!'

'You know what I mean, Susan.'

'Not entirely.' Susan's moon-face grew serious. 'You have to take happiness on trust, honey, not question every little thing, otherwise you might spoil it.' She squeezed Lorna's hand. 'Let yourself be happy with him, Lorna,' she said, 'and now we'd better get going or we'll be late for him.'

'*What!*'

Lorna started off at double speed as Susan wailed behind her, 'I was only kidding Lorna. We've got two hours yet!' But Lorna paid no attention and they arrived at the beach breathless and sticky.

Susan had been telling the truth. They did have two hours, so after they'd changed into swim-suits and rented a couple of deck chairs, which they placed in a strategic spot near the entrance to the beach, they had a swim.

The sea was clear as pale green glass, and the late afternoon sun struck the waves with streaks of gold. Lorna lay on her back and trod water, looking at the mountains that seemed to hover in the distance as if suspended in mid-air. Again she was struck by the magical quality of this country ... Jason's country, so beautiful and mysterious. Hiding the secret of a lost civilisation in its soil. Where rivers ran underground, and blood feuds still flourished.

A tiny niggle of doubt came into her mind. How did she fit into this exotic background? True, the country and Jason had enchanted her, but was enchantment a sound base for a relationship? And where exactly was this heady enchantment leading? To a summer affair ... or something more? And if it was to something more ... to marriage ... would she be capable of adapting herself to his country and its customs? From what she'd observed women played a very subservient role in Cretan society, and Lorna knew herself well enough to recognise that she wasn't the subservient type. Irritated with herself she turned over and struck out for the shore. What was she thinking of? Mooning about marriage when all that had passed between them was a few kisses and a brief confession of love. They hadn't even had time to talk properly yet. To discover each other. She was behaving like a fool.

She waded out of the water and headed for the outside shower to rinse the salt from her hair. Her skin shone like dark gold satin against the bright blue of her bikini as she strode, lithe and lovely, across the sands. A group of young men stopped playing a game of beach soccer to stare and whistle appreciatively. She ignored them, but it was comforting to know she looked good, for now that some time had elapsed since Jason's kisses she was beginning to wonder if he was having second thoughts, and by the time she was lying next to Susan (who had dozed off on her chair), she was convinced he wouldn't come.

She was sure he was regretting the whole thing and right now was trying to get a message through to the beach café to let them know he couldn't make it. Later on he would let her down lightly. But the message would come through loud and clear that he had been swept off his feet, and now realised it had all been a terrible mistake.

She was so caught up in this depressing train of thought that when he stood beside her and murmured her name she gasped, 'Jason! It's really you!' and he laughed and put his hand on her arm.

'Did I wake you *kookla*?' The touch of his warm brown hand made her skin tingle. She jerked up, hugging her knees.

'I wasn't sleeping.' He sat at the end of the chair. She felt such a surge of happiness that he was really there, looking at her so tenderly, she could have laughed aloud. 'I was just day-dreaming. Well . . . more like a nightmare really.'

'What was this nightmare?'

'Nothing.' She slid to perch beside him and slipped her arm through his. She wanted to feel the solidity of his bronzed arm against hers, to remind herself that the magic was still working. 'It was nothing. I . . . I'm glad to see you.'

He leaned over and kissed her cheek. 'That is as it should be,' he said.

She bristled a little at this. 'Nice to know I'm playing by the rules,' she said, pulling her arm away. He smiled and tucked it firmly back under his.

'It does make life easier,' he agreed, 'and now I think we should wake your sleeping duenna.' He nodded at Susan. 'I have ordered some coffee and then we should start for home. I have phoned my mother and they expect us for dinner.'

And all without consulting me, Lorna thought. But he was looking at her with such undisguised love that she bit back her irritation and said lightly. '*Endaxi*, boss-man! Let's wake sleeping beauty and get this show on the road!'

Over coffee and marvellous sticky sweets called *melogarida* Susan told them that she and Harvey had arranged to meet in Iraklion later that evening for dinner. 'You were invited too, Lorna,' she said, 'I wasn't going to ditch you.'

Jason said, 'But you will not mind if I spirit Lorna away? I suspect it will not spoil your dinner party.'

Susan grinned at him. 'I'll survive,' she said, helping herself to more *melogarida*, 'and I don't imagine you two are desolate at the thought of driving back alone.'

'One of your charms, Susan is your perceptiveness,' chuckled Jason, 'and I know you will not take it amiss if I say how happy I am that Harvey comes to Iraklion to dine.'

Susan licked her sticky fingers. 'Mmmm! It's all worked out very well,' she said, winking at Lorna, 'very well indeed.'

After arranging to deliver Susan's packages to the taverna they dropped her off at Venizelou Square and headed for home. When they had driven for a few miles, and had started to climb the steep deserted road, Jason pulled off into the shelter of the mountain, switched off the engine, and took her into his arms. 'This time we will not be interrupted,' he smiled. Lorna tried to smile back, but her heart was beating too hard for her to manage it. She felt she would suffocate from her need to feel his mouth on hers. To taste him, and feel his warm, sure hands caress her. When he bent his head over hers and brushed her lips tantalisingly lightly with his own, she moaned involuntarily, and putting her arms round his neck she pulled his mouth down on hers in a yearning kiss.

When the kiss was over he still held her close and she could feel his heart hammering under the thin cotton of his T-shirt in a wild tattoo that matched her own. She wanted him so badly it was a physical pain, and she knew that any desire she had felt in the past was a pale shadow of the real thing. She also knew that the root of this passion was love, not lust. And that she had never known an emotion like this before in her life.

'*S'agapo. S'agapo*, Lorna,' he muttered huskily, his lips brushing her ear. He gave a shuddering sigh and leaned away from her; in this light his eyes looked almost colourless. 'It is true? It is really true?'

She traced the line of his cheek with her finger. 'It's true,' she whispered and gave a little breathless laugh. 'I can't quite believe it myself, but it's true.'

He caught her hand and kissed her tracing finger, and her palm, and tasted the inside of her wrist with the tip of his tongue. Her breath caught in her throat with pleasure. 'I long to make love to you,' he murmured. 'To really make love to you.'

'Yes . . . yes . . .'

'But not in a parked car in the middle of a mountain road.' He gently pulled her ear-lobe. 'Do I not recall that you disapprove of making love in cars?'

'That seems to slip my mind when you kiss me.' She pushed her slim fingers through her hair. 'But now that you mention it I guess it is rather public . . . not to say dangerous. We don't want any more buses escorting us to the village, do we?' She was so happy to discover this other, lighter side of him she could have sung aloud.

He stroked her cheek. 'When I make you mine it must be perfect, Lorna,' he said softly, 'for us I will accept nothing less.' She nodded wordlessly, revelling in the feel of his fingers and the erotic sound of his voice. 'And now stop looking at me like that or I shall forget all my fine sentiments and take you here and now, and a fleet of buses would not stop me.' He lightly kissed her before starting the engine and heading once more into the mountains.

It was dark now and the headlights stabbed at the sun-dried rocks and patches of tough dusty grass. Jason turned on the radio and the lilting strains of bouzki music filled the car. Lorna settled back and felt the red leather seat against her naked shoulders. She closed her eyes and felt the rush of warm night air against her face. It was heavy with the scent of dittany, which is called *erontas* on the island, a Cretan variation of the word for love. Please, please don't let anything spoil this, she prayed silently. And all the way to the village she fingered the 'evil eye' charm around her throat, as a shield against misfortune.

When they left Susan's parcels at the taverna Lorna remembered her gifts for Maria and Irene. 'Oh Lord! I can't come straight back to the villa, Jason. There's something I have to do first,' she said.

'And what is that?' His eyes glinted suspiciously. 'What ... or who ... is it that you have suddenly remembered?'

'These.' She leant over and poked at the paper bags lying on the back seat. 'I have to deliver them to a friend of mine.'

'To whom?' He still looked at her with suspicion and she felt her own temper stirring.

'Hell's bells, Jason! I don't know their last name,' she snapped. 'They live in a cottage near the church.' She made a grab for the bags. 'I can walk from here.'

'No! You will not walk!' He pulled the parcels out of her hands, tearing a corner of paper in the process. 'I will drive you to these *friends*. We will make this delivery together.'

They glared at each other. 'You talk a lot about love, Jason,' she said, 'but I wonder if you really know the first thing about it?'

He went white under his tan. 'And what do you mean by that?'

'I mean that if you love someone you also trust them.' If he was pale she was not. There were two bright spots of colour on her cheeks. 'You don't trust me, do you?' When he did not answer she repeated, 'Do you?'

'*Mou Theos!* I want to Lorna,' he said desperately.

'That isn't quite the same thing is it?'

'You must understand,' he said but she ignored him.

'Did you treat Carol like this?' She glowered at him fiercely. 'Did you humiliate her too?'

The muscle in his cheek tightened. 'So you know about Carol.' She nodded. 'I had reason to doubt her,' he said.

His anger seemed to have subsided, but Lorna's had not. 'Well, I wouldn't know about that,' she said. 'But I warn you, Jason, if you won't trust me there's no future for us.' She sounded very calm, but inside she was churning with emotion.

He raked his hand through his black hair, making it stand in unruly curls. He looked suddenly like a small boy, and she relented a trifle, but she schooled herself not to reach out and touch him. He said softly, 'Does your love also include patience?'

'That too. Yes.'

'Then be patient with me, Lorna. Give me time to get used to this happiness. Remember that a few short hours ago I still believed you belonged to Nikos.'

'I belong to myself Jason.' She *had* to get this across to him. 'No matter how much I love you I will *always* belong first and foremost to myself.'

'Spoken like a true emancipated American woman,' he said, with a return to something of his old manner.

'CANADIAN!'

'The same thing.'

'Not the same thing at all,' she flashed, her eyes cobalt with irritation. He gave her a lop-sided smile and tried to take her into his arms, but she remained stiff and unyielding, although part of her longed to feel his arms round her again.

'If I was jealous for a moment I apologise,' he said formally, pulling away from her. 'Blame my stupid Cretan nature.'

'We can't help our natures. We're born with them . . . and then we're stuck with them!' She hadn't meant to say that, it was cruel and stupid. But it was as if she was on an icy toboggan slide, she seemed unable to stop herself.

'I understand you,' he said, so grimly that all the

fight went out of her. 'Now we will deliver your parcel.
As it is we shall be late for dinner.'

'Do . . . do you still want me to come to dinner?' she
faltered. 'I mean . . . if you'd rather not . . .'

He replied tersely, 'My mother expects you.' Lorna
didn't say another word.

Within minutes they arrived at the cottage. It was
night now and light gleamed through chinks in the
shutters. Jason said, 'I did not know you knew Maria
Koronakis,' but she didn't reply.

Maria came to the door, hastily buttoning her
dress. She had apparently been getting ready for bed.
Lorna knew most of the villages retired with the sun,
and she cursed herself for wasting all that time in a
destructive argument with Jason, and now disturbing
her friend. But Maria seemed cheerful enough when
she saw who her visitors were. She was particularly
glad to see Jason, and ushered them into the kitchen
with great ceremony, pulling out two of her small
rush-bottomed chairs and dusting them off for her
guests.

Irene poked her head out from the sleeping room at
the back. She was already in her nightdress. When she
saw Jason she gave a squeal of pleasure and hurled
herself at him.

'Irene . . . *ochi*,' her mother admonished, taking a
black shawl from the back of a chair and wrapping it
round the child's shoulders.

Jason lifted the little girl on to his knee and said
something in Greek that sent her into a gale of giggles,
then she sat, wrapped in her mother's shawl, beaming at
the company.

In very halting Greek Lorna presented Maria with
her presents. At first the woman was silent, her large
dark eyes intent, as first the sandals, then the dresses
and hair-ribbons were unwrapped. For a moment
Lorna wondered if she had offended her, but when
Maria gave a strangled sob, and hugged and kissed her

she knew that it was simply emotion that had kept her quiet for so long.

'Hold on a minute,' Lorna said, slipping into English and presenting the box of candy, 'this is for you.'

'Ah! . . . you lovely . . . crazy . . .' Maria laughed, and tearing off the lid offered the sweets to her guests and cried, and mopped her eyes all at the same time.

Irene, who had climbed off Jason's lap when her gifts were produced, was already wearing her sandals and doing a dance around the kitchen table, holding one of her new dresses against her thin little body, the shawl trailing behind her like a shadow.

Jason and Lorna each accepted a candy, then Jason said it was time to be going. Maria took his hand in both of hers and chattered excitedly for a few more minutes, nodding towards the Canadian girl. Then she kissed Lorna again and whispered, '*Dombros* . . . a good man, eh?' And Lorna nodded, but her heart felt heavy, contrasting her euphoric frame of mind when she chose these presents, and the strain she felt with Jason now.

Maria and her daughter escorted them to the garden gate and waved as the sleek white car glided carefully over the bumpy track. Once they were on the road Jason asked her, 'Maria tells me she is teaching you Greek. Is this true?'

'Of course it's true. But I'm a very slow pupil.'

'She does not think so. And I was most impressed with your attempts to speak it just now.'

'Thank you . . . *'efharisto*.' She hoped this was his way of offering her an olive branch.

'Why do you bother?'

'I beg your pardon?'

'I ask why you bother to learn my language? You do not need it on the dig surely?' He sounded so cold her hope of an olive branch withered before it blossomed.

'No, I don't need it on the dig. But I will need it if I'm to travel in remote parts of Greece for my book.'

She had been thinking of taking off in the autumn

and exploring the rest of Crete, and also inland Greece, but until that moment she hadn't actually made up her mind. Now her disappointment that their quarrel was still unresolved crystallised her decision.

'Book?' he said. 'What book is this?'

'A photographic look at the country,' she answered vaguely, 'I haven't quite worked it out yet.'

'And you plan to visit remote areas you say?'

'Oh! Absolutely! Nothing "touristy" for me.' She could sense that her assumed nonchalance was getting to him, and she was perversely gratified.

His fingers gripped the wheel. 'Do you not realise that it is extremely unwise for a woman to go alone to such regions?'

'Don't patronise me, Jason,' she said with airy detachment. 'I'll have you know that back home I drove from coast to coast by myself, and I didn't have any trouble.'

'That was Canada not Crete,' he insisted. 'I tell you that here it is not safe for a woman alone.'

'Well, I don't have any choice,' she said flatly, 'besides I think you exaggerate.'

'I DO NOT!' Viciously he jabbed at the accelerator and swerved the car on to the villa's flower-bordered drive. The rear wheels spun for a moment, causing a shower of grit to fly behind them. 'I do not exaggerate,' he said, 'it is you who do not . . . *will* not . . . understand. This is still a savage and sometimes dangerous land. And with your blonde beauty . . . you command attention.'

'You're trying to tell me that I'm just a foreigner in your country, aren't you?' The stone that was her heart was getting heavier.

He stopped the car at the front of the house. 'Not *just* a foreigner, but a stranger to our ways certainly.'

'Oh! There's such a gulf between us,' she cried forlornly, 'you make me feel so . . . so lonely.'

'You do not need to feel lonely *kookla mou*.' The anger had gone from him as suddenly as it had flared.

She hunched in the seat and stared miserably at the velvet black night. 'But we're so different,' she said at last. 'It's as if there's an ocean between us . . . and we just shout to each other from separate ships.'

'Then let us jump into the water and swim towards each other,' he said. 'Then we will meet. *Ne?*'

She gave him the ghost of a smile. 'What about sharks?' she said.

'No sharks, I promise.' He kissed the tip of her nose. 'Only porpoises.'

'I'm very fond of porpoises,' she whispered.

Putting his arm round her shoulders he said softly, 'Shall we try, Lorna? To have patience and to swim towards each other.'

Not trusting herself to speak she nodded, her eyes suspiciously bright. He kissed her mouth and held her gently against his broad chest like a child who needs comforting, stroking her silky hair until she relaxed against him. After a while he said, 'We had better go in. They will be waiting for us.'

Obediently she let him lead her up the shallow steps to the house. Before he opened the door he looked at her searchingly for a moment. 'Do not worry *kookla mou*,' he said, 'everything is going to be all right.'

She made herself smile up at him and say, 'Of course it is, darling.' But she knew in her heart that it was going to take more than a blue glass charm to ward off the storms and perils that threatened this tempestuous love affair she had embarked upon.

CHAPTER EIGHT

MORNINGS were always glorious in Crete, but the morning of Ariadne's wedding seemed particularly so. The air was fresh, and golden fingers of sunlight lit the distant hills.

Although it was still early the villa was buzzing with activity when Lorna woke. Maids bustled about with bundles of freshly ironed linen, or with trays bearing plates and glasses, or with vases of brightly coloured flowers. The Peritakis cook was being helped by several women hired from the village, and from the kitchen regions came the steady hum of conversation, accompanied by much clanging and banging, and the sweet smell of baking.

Outside several workers from the orange groves had been dragooned into helping the gardeners put up long trestle tables under the plane trees for the wedding feast. Already an old man was lighting the charcoal in one of the pits dug specially for the occasion. Before long he and his friends would take turns to rotate the spit, gazing almost entranced while the meat sputtered over the smouldering charcoal.

Lorna hastily flung on a pair of slacks and a shirt, and grabbing her camera went in search of pictures— and a morning cup of coffee if she was lucky. She found her coffee—an electric kettle and a tin of Nescafé on the kitchen counter—and took several shots of the general activity before returning upstairs to knock gingerly on Ariadne's door, which was opened by Madam Peritakis, who greeted her warmly.

'Poor child!' she said, 'you did not have much chance to sleep this morning with all the noise.'

Knowing that Jason's mother was not unaware of the

127

growing affection between her son and her Canadian guest this friendliness was particularly welcome. 'Who would want to sleep on an important day like this?' Lorna smiled.

'I have not slept all the night,' piped Ariadne who was sitting on the end of her bed, her face pale with excitement. She was wearing a pair of blue cotton pyjamas and looked about fourteen years old. She looks awfully young to get married, Lorna thought. Why! she's hardly out of the schoolroom.

Madam Peritakis said, 'I cannot enforce your sleeping habits, Ariadne, but I do insist that you eat *some* breakfast.' She gestured to a silver tray that stood untouched on the bedside table. 'Otherwise you will faint before you get to the church.'

Ariadne looked at her mother rebelliously. 'I will not faint, Mama,' she said.

Lorna took one of the small sesame rolls from the tray and bit into it. 'Why don't I share your breakfast?' she suggested. 'I'm not going to be married so I'm starving.'

The young girl giggled, but she took the other roll and nibbled at it delicately. This token gesture seemed to satisfy her mother. '*Kala!*' she said. 'Now that is settled I will see if they have finished ironing your dress. Then it will be time for your bath. No! Stay!' she commanded Lorna, who had moved tentatively towards the door. 'It is good that you are here. Both Ariadne and I are nervous this morning. Your presence calms us, I think.'

Lorna held up her camera. 'As long as I'm not in the way maybe I could start taking some pictures?'

'A good idea,' agreed Madam Peritakis, and clutching her lace dressing-gown to her ample bosom she left the two girls.

'Photographs before I am in my wedding dress?' Ariadne looked down at her crumpled pyjamas.

'Sure! Let's get a record of the whole day. You can

always discard any prints you don't like. And don't *pose* for me,' she said, for Ariadne had straightened up and smoothed her hair when Lorna looked through the viewfinder.

'It is hard to ignore a camera,' the Greek girl grumbled. She stretched towards the tray to pour herself a glass of orange juice and Lorna caught the glint of jewels at her throat. 'I am not like a professional model.'

In an attempt to take her mind off the ordeal of being photographed Lorna asked, 'What's that round your neck?' Ariadne pulled aside the collar of her pyjama top to reveal a necklace of aquamarines. 'Do you always wear jewellery to bed?'

'Mama gave them to me this morning. They belonged to her. They were a wedding gift from her father.'

Lorna admired their watery fire. 'They're lovely.'

'For Jason's bride there will be emeralds,' Ariadne informed her.

'That's nice,' Lorna said, wondering why she felt suddenly defensive.

'Do you have such a tradition in your family Lorna?'

'We're not exactly in that league,' Lorna replied gruffly, screwing up one blue eye and concentrating on the viewfinder of her camera.

Ariadne looked puzzled. 'What does that mean? I do not understand this . . . league?'

'It means that we don't have any jewels to give away in our family,' Lorna said. 'We're not rich at all.'

'But you wear lovely jewellery,' the other girl insisted. 'Much silver, and at the party some very pretty turquoises. I noted them particularly.'

'They were my mother's.' She pressed the button and rewound the film.

'You see!' Ariadne crowed, 'Your mother also gave you jewels.'

In an effort to get Ariadne off the subject Lorna said,

'Just lean against the pillows will you, and moisten your lips for this next shot?'

'I thought you told me I was not to pose,' Ariadne reminded her.

'Yes ... well ... Just for this one. Because of ... of the light on the pillows,' Lorna improvised.

Dutifully Ariadne licked her lips and lay against the linen-covered pillows. Then she said, 'Does it upset you that we are rich?'

Somewhat taken aback Lorna blustered. 'Upset me? Of course it doesn't.' She took a couple of pictures and was conscious of Ariadne's steady green gaze staring back at her.

'I think it does,' she said, 'but we were not always rich. My great-grandfather was a poor peasant. Everything we have we have earned. We are not ... how do you say it? *Autocrats.*'

Putting aside her camera Lorna squatted on the end of the bed. 'I'm sorry, Ariadne,' she said, 'I'm behaving like a pig. You're quite right. I do get uptight when I think of the differences between us.'

'I do not see any differences,' the young girl smiled. 'I wear my mother's aquamarines and you wear your mother's turquoises.'

'But you're Cretan and I'm Canadian,' Lorna muttered.

With a laugh Ariadne bounced down to the end of the bed to sit next to her friend. 'And we are both women and consequently share the same feelings.' She put her arm round Lorna's hunched shoulders. 'Do you know what I think? I think that you have the soul of a peasant, Lorna. You distrust anything that is unfamiliar. But we are peasants too! So you see there can be no differences between us.'

'You make it sound so simple.' Morosely Lorna fastened her camera case.

'It is simple,' insisted Ariadne. 'And now stop looking so serious on my wedding day or I shall be most cross.' Her eyes, so like Jason's, twinkled mischievously. 'And I am horrible when I am cross for I too have the Peritakis temper.'

The door flew open and Madam Peritakis, a galleon in full sail, burst in. 'The hairdresser has arrived,' she announced. 'Quickly Ariadne. You must have your bath and then get dressed.'

Lorna headed for the door. 'I'll leave you in peace,' she said.

'I do not mean to drive you away, Lorna,' Madam Peritakis smiled assuringly.

'You're not, but I want to get some more pictures of the preparations outside,' Lorna told her. But in truth she had an overwhelming longing to see Jason. She wanted to stand close to him and feel the magic his presence always gave her.

She went first to the back of the house. Vasily was just driving up in his battered old *mikani* which was loaded with trays of *keftehes*—cold rissoles flavoured with ouzo and lying under a cover of lemon leaves. The *mikani* also contained a huge basket of bread and many sharp and unfamiliar cheeses. He greeted Lorna cheerfully and bustled into the house.

There were many strange cars parked in the drive, and donkeys tethered under the trees, and a constant coming and going of people carrying chairs and flowers and the impedimenta of a large party. She took several photographs of this cheerful industry and then made her way to the trestle tables that had been put up under the plane trees. From there she caught a glimpse of Jason's broad back. He was standing a little way down the garden, gazing out across the valley. When he heard her footsteps he turned.

'Lorna! *Kalimera*, my darling.' He took her hand and tucked it under his arm. 'I was just thinking,' he said, 'I was thinking how quickly the years pass. I carried Ariadne on my shoulders through those groves. She was a baby, and it seems like yesterday. And now it is time for me to hand her over to the care of a husband.'

Privately Lorna thought he made his sister sound like a parcel being delivered from one household to another, but she merely said, 'Kosti seems very nice though,' and let it go at that.

'He is a fine man,' Jason agreed, 'I shall be happy to have him for my brother. And it is a love match. That too is most fortunate.'

'And if it wasn't would you still be happy to have Kosti for your brother?' Lorna asked, and when he looked at her searchingly she continued, 'I mean would you expect Ariadne to marry someone the family chose, rather than someone she had chosen for herself?'

'Do you really believe that I would force Ariadne to marry against her will?' he said, pained.

'Well ... no ... but marriages are sometimes still arranged in Crete, aren't they?'

'Certainly. And usually they are successful. You North Americans have such a horror of arranged marriages. Yet my parents had a long and happy marriage ... which was arranged by my grandparents.' His jaw jutted squarely. 'I would point out that our divorce rate is a tenth of yours,' he said.

'That's not fair!' She was beginning to feel irked by him. 'I'll bet there are lots of unhappy marriages in Crete, but because it's so much harder to get a divorce in this country ... especially for the woman ... people just don't try.'

'It is unfortunate you do not yet read Greek well enough to understand the newspapers,' he said loftily, 'for then you would know that our divorce laws have recently changed. One can now obtain divorce by common consent after a separation of four years. Also the dowry has been eliminated.'

'You mean wives are no longer rated in goats and olive trees,' she said acidly.

His hand tightened on her arm. 'There are times when I would like to shake you, Lorna,' he said. 'Shake some sense into that beautiful blonde head of yours.'

'I don't think I'm without sense.' She stood rigid.

'Perhaps not. But you are most unfair. Not once do you ask me how *I* feel about these matters. It might surprise you to learn that I have always felt the dowry to be a cruel tradition. I also believe that in the past the lack of rights for the wife has been unjust. But because I live in a village in Crete you assume—without even asking my opinion—that I subscribe without thought to the old ways. You insult me *kookla mou*,' he finished quietly.

'I don't mean to insult you. But you're very proud of being Cretan. That includes the old traditions surely,' she persisted.

He nodded. 'Some of them certainly. And I do not like *strident* women.'

'Who does?' She shrugged her shoulders.

'You spoke of Carol last night.' He continued to gaze across the valley. 'One of her less agreeable characteristics was a certain stridency.'

'Your mother thought you and Carol might marry.'

'My mother is an imaginative woman.'

She freed herself from his encircling arm. 'Come on, Jason, don't give me that! You're not going to deny that you were attracted to her, are you?' Please deny it, she prayed silently.

'Of course I was attracted to her. She was beautiful and I am a normal man.' He looked down at Lorna through half-shut eyes. 'But I soon learned that marriage to such a one as Carol would have been a grave mistake. It would have led to unhappiness for both of us.'

'Because she was a North American?' Like I am, she thought silently.

'Because she was *Carol*!' His patience was fraying. 'And because she refused to accept me ... or my background. She wanted to take everything except my heritage. It was an impossible situation.'

'It must have hurt you though ... at the time.' It was

like rubbing salt into an open wound to even think of his feelings for Carol, but she seemed powerless to stop herself.

He replied with a jauntiness she found disconcerting. 'Not particularly. In the long run it meant nothing more than the end of some pleasant summer madness.'

'Pleasant summer madness,' she repeated, and the phrase struck chill in her heart.

He put his arm round her shoulders again, and together they started walking slowly towards the house. Sunshine filtered through the leaves, causing discs of gold to dance on the path ahead. 'And what of your past, Lorna?' he said. 'How is it that someone as beautiful as you has not married?'

'Oh! I've been asked a couple of times,' she tried to sound offhand. 'I nearly made it to the altar once but . . .'

'But?' He looked down at her and now his eyes were serious.

'I thought better of it,' she said lightly.

'Because of your career?'

'Something like that,' she agreed, and he gripped her elbow and started to walk faster.

I wonder why I don't tell him the real reason, she thought. Why don't I tell him that Jon didn't want to look after me. Ever. And part of me wants to be taken care of even though I'm quite capable of taking care of myself. If I'd married Jon I would have had to be the strong one . . . the dominant partner . . . and I don't want that. But she seemed incapable of finding the right words, so she said nothing.

They reached the patio and Jason glanced at the wafer-thin watch on his brown wrist. 'It is time for us to get ready.' Sadly Lorna sensed that he had distanced himself from her a little.

'See you at the church!' she said with forced gaiety, and he smiled, but his eyes were sombre.

She made her way upstairs to her room aware that a

tiny personal cloud was now hovering over her. Being in love with Jason Peritakis wasn't easy, she reflected, but she knew that if he was cautious with her now it was her own fault. She had done nothing to dispel the image of a woman concerned solely with her own career. A woman who viewed marriage as a trap to be avoided. Little wonder he had retreated.

When she had showered and dressed she stood for a moment holding her blue-glass charm against the bodice of her dress, then she slipped the chain over her silky head. Fortunately the 'evil eye' was hidden by her collar, for it clashed with the violet chiffon gown. She knew she was being childish by continuing to wear this gaudy talisman, but she didn't feel like tempting fate by discarding it. One day she knew she'd throw the stupid thing away. But not yet!

The first glimpse she had of the bride was in the downstairs sitting room. Ariadne stood, still as a statue in white silk organza. A circlet of pearls was wound around her top-knot of glossy black hair, and from it a short veil floated like a drift of mist. She held a bunch of creamy honeysuckle blossoms mixed with some of the purple flowers that bloomed outside the dark-room. She was incandescent with joy.

'How beautiful you look,' said Lorna, surprised to find that she had a lump in her throat at the sight of this radiant young bride.

'The dress is most successful I think,' said Madam Peritakis, materialising from a corner. She spoke with deliberate casualness but this didn't fool Lorna, who could tell that beneath her calm exterior she was surging with emotion.

'It's more than the dress.' Taking her camera from its case Lorna said to Ariadne, 'You're shining like a hundred candles,' and the girl smiled softly. She seemed to *quiver* with happiness. Again emotion washed over Lorna, and she had to swallow hard. 'Why don't I take a photo of you with your mother,' she said gruffly, and

busied herself arranging them in a suitable pose. 'Your
flowers are lovely, Ariadne,' she said when she'd got her
voice under control, 'I recognise the honeysuckle, of
course, but what are the other ones? I don't know
them.'

'They were Jason's idea,' Ariadne said. 'I wanted my
wedding bouquet to be from our garden, and he
suggested to use some of the flowers from the Chaste
Tree ... the one that grows near your dark-room. He
said it would be appropriate.' She blushed.

'I should hope so, indeed,' replied her mother,
smoothing her grey silk. She smiled fondly at her child.
'It was a most ... perceptive ... thought of your
brother.'

Lorna knew of the store Cretan men set on their
bride's chastity, and she refrained from asking if the
bride had the same expectations with regards to her
groom. She knew that such a question would be
incomprehensible to Madam Peritakis and Ariadne,
and that today of all days was not the time to discuss
the matter, but the thought of such a blatant double
standard rankled nevertheless. To take her mind off this
inequality she took rather more pictures than she had
originally intended.

After a while there was a tap at the door and one of
the maids, dressed in her best, came into the room. She
exclaimed over her young mistress's appearance and
then exchanged a few words with Madam Peritakis,
who nodded and sent her on her way.

'It is time for us to go,' Madam Peritakis told Lorna.
'The car is waiting for me, but perhaps you will wish to
take photographs of Ariadne and Jason as they walk to
the church.'

'Mama ... your flower!' Ariadne cried, picking a
single crimson rose from a vase and breaking the stem
short. With great ceremony she presented it to her
mother, who solemnly kissed her on the forehead before
pinning the flower on the traditional right side of her

dress. Tactfully Lorna withdrew, leaving mother and daughter together.

When she reached the road she could see knots of people, some of them servants from the villa, walking purposefully down towards the village. They were all dressed in their finery, and many of the older ones wore national costume, the women's dark dresses embroidered at the cuffs and collars. The old men, many of them riding donkeys, proudly showed off their high boots which were polished to the gloss of chestnuts for the occasion.

Lorna walked down the hill too, greeting people as she went, then she perched herself on a rock to be in a good position for photographing the arrival of the bride.

She could see the church from here. Everyone who could cram themselves inside had done so, and the rest were gathered outside the door like bees round a hive. She could see Susan and Harvey among them, also the figure of Kosti, elegant in a dark lounge suit, a flower in his buttonhole, waiting by the church door.

Sitting alone under a vaulted blue sky she raised her camera and focused on the last curve of the road. But when the bride and her brother finally appeared she lowered it, for her hand had started to tremble.

In the brilliant light Ariadne's dress, white as icing-sugar against the pavement, seemed to shimmer, making her look like a creature from another world. But it was not the sight of Ariadne that dazzled Lorna. It was Jason who took her breath away. He was dressed in full Cretan costume. Wide breeches of black silk, and round his lithe waist was wound a dark red cummerbund. His shirt of spotless white silk contrasted starkly with the sober black of his well-cut jacket. His black boots shone like polished jet. On his head he wore the traditional small black silk turban with a fringe of blackest beads that fell over his wide forehead. She could see the silver handle of a dagger glinting from his waistband. He had never looked more magnificent. The whole impression was one of elegant ferocity. He looked like a handsome eighteenth-century brigand. Dangerous and exciting.

Hastily Lorna recovered herself and followed the couple with her camera. When they reached the place where Kosti stood waiting, Jason placed his sister's hand in her groom's. Smiling, Kosti kissed her on the mouth, and then led her into the church with Jason following them.

Lorna put away her camera and edged through the crowd. The little church was jammed, but she managed to manoeuvre herself inside the door, so that she had a view of the bridal pair standing at the altar. Four little girls dressed in white, wreaths of flowers in their hair, held thick candles that glowed fitfully. The candles were set in holders manufactured out of yards and yards of frothing white gauze, like a ballet dancer's tutu. Perfume from the mass of flowers that decorated the church blended with the aromatic scent of incense. A bearded priest, his gold brocade vestment gleaming richly in the flickering light, conducted the ceremony. There was no music, only the chanting of the priest and the intermittent tinkling of a bell. Fragile wreaths of lemon blossom were placed on the heads of the couple and changed over three times.

Lorna's eyes grew misty. She thought she had never witnessed anything so beautiful. She watched through a blur of tears as the gold wedding-bands were placed on their fingers and then also passed between them three times. There was a stir in the congregation, a collective sigh as Kosti and his radiant bride became husband and wife.

Lorna stumbled out into the sunshine blinking away her tears. What *is* the matter with me? she thought, I know it's the done thing to cry at weddings but this is *ridiculous*! She shied away from the knowledge that the reason she was so moved was because she envied

Ariadne her open declaration of love. She longed, with every fibre of her being, to stand next to Jason, as Ariadne stood so proudly next to her new husband, bound to him forever by a sacred and solemn ritual.

Susan came up to her. 'What a lovely wedding, eh, Lorna?' When Lorna didn't immediately reply she peered at her friend's wet eyes and said, 'Really got to you, eh?'

'You could say that,' Lorna agreed, wiping her eyes on a tissue, 'Guess I'm getting sentimental in my old age.'

'Nothing wrong with that,' smiled Susan, 'if I could have got into the church and seen the ceremony I would have wept buckets. Weddings just *wipe* me out.'

'How are you around new babies?'

'Mush,' she confessed smugly.

'You are a kind, nice girl "Susie Q",' Lorna teased, unfastening her camera case, 'remind me to buy you a raincoat for your next wedding.'

'I'd rather you helped me buy a wedding dress,' Susan said breathlessly.

Lorna stopped fiddling with her camera. 'Susie! You mean you and Harvey?'

Susan nodded vigorously. 'Mind you it's not official yet. But he asked me if I'd think about it, and I said I would. Not that I need to,' she babbled happily, 'there's no doubt in my mind. We're really crazy about each other and we have so much in common . . .'

'Yes,' said Lorna wistfully, 'yes, you do.'

Further talk was impossible for at that moment Ariadne and Kosti came out of the church. The crowd gave a roar and the four little girls rushed ahead of the bride and groom in order to pelt them with rice and flowers. The couple laughed and ducked under this barrage, then Kosti kissed his wife to the accompaniment of another loud cheer, and they set off on foot up to the villa, followed by the entire village.

Jason, head and shoulders taller than the crowd

around him, elbowed his way to Lorna's side. 'There you are *kookla mou*! Have you managed to get many pictures?' he asked.

'Two rolls of film so far,' She slapped at her duffle bag.

'Let me carry that for you.' He slung the bag over his own wide shoulder. 'And how do you enjoy our little country wedding so far?'

'Little! I should think half of Crete is here,' she chuckled.

'And a good part of Athens, too,' he smiled.

'It's a beautiful wedding, Jason. I'd like one just like it.' Thinking that sounded shamefully like begging she amended it by adding, 'If I ever had to get married, I mean.'

'You make it sound like a punishment,' he said.

She could tell he wasn't joking but she attempted to keep the tone light. 'You mean like locking oneself in a padded cell and throwing away the key?'

'Is that how you view the married state?' His mouth set grimly.

'I've never given the married state much thought to tell the truth.' She ran a few paces ahead of him. 'Let me get a few shots of you in that costume,' she called, retreating behind her camera and clicking away like mad.

He reached her in three strides. 'You will not always be able to hide behind that thing, Lorna,' he said tightly. 'One day life will catch up with you, and then you will find a camera poor company I think.'

'It's been pretty good company so far.' She had to fight to keep her voice from wobbling, for the ignominious tears that had overwhelmed her in church threatened to return.

'Then I will leave you with it.' Savagely he thrust her bag back on to her shoulders. 'I will not trespass on your . . . your professional time any more.'

'Jason, for pity's sake!' she croaked feebly, but he had already gone.

Two salty tears spilled out of her eyes and trailed
down her cheeks. She dashed them away with the back
of her hand. 'Blast, blast, *blast*!' she muttered,
deliberately goading herself into a temper in order to
control her stupid emotions. He had totally mis-
understood her. But she confessed it would have taken
a mind-reader to comprehend what she had really
meant. In attempting to salvage her own pride, she'd
wounded his. It was her pride at work again. Her
stubborn empty pride.

Drained of all zest she raised her camera again and
scanned the thinning crowd, and it was through her
viewfinder that she glimpsed Jason's tall figure. He had
turned back and was hurrying towards her. When he
reached her side he said, 'Lorna, I cannot bear to
quarrel with you.'

She was so astounded that Jason ... Jason of the
proud Cretan heritage ... had returned to apologise
that she could only stare up at him through wide blue
eyes, her lashes starred with tears.

'Lorna ... *agapi mou* ... you have been crying.'

Her habit of pride made her say involuntarily, 'No!'
Then she gave a sigh and admitted, 'Yes. A bit.'

'Oh! My darling,' he drew her to him and gently
stroked her hair, ignoring the interested stares of the
trailing villagers. Lorna felt like a child that had been
lost and was at last safe at home. 'Forgive me, Lorna,'
he whispered. 'Forgive me. I cannot bear to hurt you.'

'I was thoughtless,' she mumbled into his silk shirt-
front, 'I'm the one who should be asking for
forgiveness.'

He cupped her face in his strong brown hand. 'Let us
not argue about that as well,' he smiled wryly. 'Let us
simply forgive each other and be friends again. *Ne?*'

She nodded mistily. 'Friends.' Her smile came out
like the sun from behind a cloud.

'*Etsi!* And now we must hurry or they will start the
feast without us.' Once more he took her duffle bag and

firmly grasping her hand he asked, 'Your sandals? Are they strong enough for running?'

'Well, they're not up to Olympic standards,' she waggled a foot at him, 'but they'll do I guess.'

He grinned. 'Then hang on to me. Who knows, we may yet win a gold medal,' and they ran the rest of the way, laughing together like children.

People were already sitting at the long tables under the plane trees when Jason led Lorna to a chair at the bride's table. He took his place beside his mother, who was seated as custom dictated next to her daughter. Madam Peritakis looked shrewdly at the flushed face of her Canadian house guest, and Lorna felt herself colour to an even brighter pink under the older woman's scrutiny. Then Madam Peritakis lifted her glass of wine. 'To Lorna,' she said warmly, 'to Lorna who is more to us than a guest. *Ochi?*' She smiled discerningly at her son, and Lorna felt a surge of happiness.

Jason raised his glass and before drinking poured a little of his wine on to the ground. 'To give thanks to the gods for a good harvest,' he told Lorna. 'A Cretan farmer always gives a little back to the earth.'

'I think that's only right and proper,' Lorna said, pouring a generous splash from her own glass, while Jason and her fellow diners laughed and applauded.

Nikos, who had been glaring resentfully at Jason said, 'I do not waste my wine in such silly superstitions.'

'It might be a good idea for you if you did,' Lorna snapped without thinking. There was a ripple of suppressed laughter round the table.

'We should perhaps copy the ancients and dilute our wine with water,' Jason broke in diplomatically, topping up his glass from the water jug. Lorna did the same. '*Pan metro arasto* ... Nothing to excess.' He smiled at his glowering cousin. 'To your good health Nikos!' But Nikos refused to acknowledge the toast.

The meal was lengthy, and noisy, and fun. They ate roast lamb, and kid flavoured with herbs and garlic.

There were platters of stuffed tomatoes, and purple-skinned aubergines, crisp mountains of fried potatoes and bowls of tossed salad tangy with feta cheese and olives. There were runner beans, and onions and carrots. There were red, green and yellow peppers all bathed in oil and lemon juice, and cucumbers in yoghurt. And when all that had been cleared away there were the sweet dishes. First a gigantic wedding cake that the bridal pair cut with Jason's dagger. Athenian walnut cake in honour of the bridegroom, and chocolate cake, and marbled slabs of *halvah*, brittle and tooth-curlingly sweet. And tray after tray of pastries wrapped in gold and silver and scarlet paper, tempting and luscious. And then, when the last dish had been pushed aside, and the wedding cake was reduced to a scattering of crumbs, large silver dishes heaped with pink and white sugared almonds were offered to the guests.

Lorna shook her head. 'Oh! I couldn't,' she said, 'I couldn't eat another mouthful.'

'You must take at least one, Lorna,' Ariadne called from across the table. 'Not to eat. To put under your pillow tonight. For then you will dream of the man you will marry.'

'We do the same with wedding cake. Sugared almonds aren't nearly as messy, I must say.' She helped herself to a pink one and put it in her pocket. 'I'll probably dream of somebody quite unsuitable. I always do.'

Now people pushed their chairs back and sipped their wine and toyed with the wilting flowers that decorated the tables. Then Professor Spanakis took out a guitar and started to play. The local baker produced a violin and backed by their own accompaniment they started to sing in rhyming couplets.

Jason quietly came round and pulled a chair up beside her. 'They are singing *mantinades*,' he said. 'Have you heard of them? They are handed down from generation to generation and adapted for special occasions. Listen carefully and you will recognise some of the names.' He took her hand and absently played with her slender fingers, and Lorna thought that she had never been so happy in her life. The late afternoon sun backed the scene in soft gold, and the antiphonal chanting of the two men wove a thin pattern of sound that seemed to bind her and Jason and the wedding guests in a tapestry that was as old as time. She recognised Ariadne's name, and Kosti's, and Jason's was sung out.

He loosed her hand then and took up the song himself. He had a pleasant light baritone, untrained but true. Then she heard him sing her own name, incorporated into the verse, and a chill of pleasure ran through her. At the other side of the table she saw Ariadne smile and raise her glass to her brother.

The music died and for a few seconds there was a hush. Then four musicians from the village started to play waltzes. The bride and groom started the dance, and soon the grass was crowded with whirling couples. Jason put his arm round her waist and they joined in.

They danced well together, even on this rough terrain, and Lorna revelled in the feel of his strong arm around her, and his hard lithe body pressed against hers. The dance grew faster, and laughing she finally begged off. 'I've had too much wine, Jason ... if I go any faster I'll fall over.'

They left the dancing area and stood under the trees. He brought her a glass of fresh lemonade which she gratefully sipped, enjoying its astringent bite on her palate.

He smoothed a strand of flaxen hair from her warm face. 'It is hard for me to leave your side but I must dance with some of our guests *kookla mou*,' he said. He leaned over her and his wine-scented breath fanned her cheek. 'But if you dance with any of those Athenian louts,' he indicated the group of young men who had partnered her the night of the engagement party, 'I will kill you.' He smiled, but there was menace in his voice.

'Then you will go to prison, won't you Jason?' she said calmly, tilting her chin and staring up at him.

He paused for the length of a heartbeat. 'It would make me very angry to see you dance with one of them,' he said.

'Even if, while I danced, I was telling him about us?'

'About us? I do not see . . .'

'Think about it, Jason.' She stood on tiptoe and kissed his cheek. 'Remember that I love you,' she said, 'but that doesn't give you the right to tell me who I may or may not dance with.'

He put his hands on her shoulders and his palms felt warm through the thin chiffon. 'That is technically correct,' he agreed, 'you do have a perfect right to choose your own dance partners. Just remember that I would prefer it if you refused your Athenian admirers.' He lightly brushed her forehead with his lips and walked away.

Lorna gave a small sigh and let herself relax. At least that particular skirmish hadn't developed into a quarrel. And while she hadn't exactly won the war, she thought she had given him food for thought. Maybe she would learn to handle Jason after all. To fit into his world. She knew she loved him enough to make compromises . . . if he would just learn to do the same . . .

'Wow! I think I must have lost twenty pounds!' Susan staggered up, Harvey at her side, panting from their enthusiastic waltzing. 'What's that you're drinking?'

'Lemonade. Jason got it for me.'

'Honey, would you get some for us?' Susan begged the breathless Harvey.

'Sure thing,' he puffed, 'your wish is my command Princess,' he winked at the two girls. 'What about you, Lorna? Would you like another?'

Lorna shook her head and her satiny hair swung. 'No thanks.'

'Why don't we sit down,' Susan said. She spied a group of garden chairs. 'We'll be over there, honey. Okay?'

The two girls settled themselves and gazed lazily at the dancers. Lorna noticed the figure of Nikos slouching away through the orange groves. Probably not enough booze for him here, she thought, and then dismissed him from her mind.

'What a great party,' Susan sighed, 'I've *never* had such a good time!'

'Terrific,' Lorna agreed.

'And how about old Spanakis? Singing those songs an' all? Who would have believed he could be like that?'

This reminded Lorna that Jason had included her name in the *mantinades*, and her full mouth curved in secret pleasure. 'Mmmm! Professor Spanakis does seem to be in a good mood,' she said.

'Good? He's positively *angelic*! He even danced with me,' Susan informed her.

'Wonders will never cease!' grinned Lorna. 'It must be the effect of the wedding.'

'That and the little head,' Susan answered, fanning herself with a plump hand.

Lorna looked at her blankly. 'The little head?'

The fanning stopped. 'Of course! You don't know about the new find. Thank you, honey,' she said to Harvey, who joined them at this moment with two glasses of lemonade. 'Lorna doesn't know about the little head,' she told him as she started to sip.

'Harvey, what is she talking about?' Lorna appealed to him. 'You tell me. I can't get any sense out of her.'

'Well, yesterday afternoon, while you two were gallivanting about in Iraklion, we made the best find yet.' Seating himself next to his lady-love he started to drink his lemonade.

'Well? Go on!' Lorna said impatiently. This leisurely couple would soon drive her mad.

After a great gulp, he continued, 'A small terracotta head of a woman. Most of the paint worn off, but still in remarkable condition. Hardly chipped at all. At a guess I'd say dating from the middle Minoan period. Once fixed to some kind of pedestal, it must have stood about three inches high. Does that answer your question?'

'But that's wonderful,' Lorna cried, 'I can't wait to see it.'

'Well, you'll get to photograph it on Monday,' Susan reminded her.

'Yeah! Then it's going straight to the museum,' Harvey volunteered. 'Spanakis even played with the idea of sending it there Friday night, but I think he wanted to gloat over it this weekend. But it's all very hush-hush. We're not to tell anybody who's not connected with the dig. For security reasons.' He took another swallow.

'I wonder if Jason knows,' Lorna asked.

'I guess Spanakis will tell him sometime,' Harvey said, 'seeing it's on his land and all.'

The three of them stayed chatting for a few more minutes, then Lorna excused herself and went in search of Jason. She wanted to share this piece of news with him. Because of his financial backing, and his special interest in the history of the island, she knew this particular discovery would give him pleasure.

She found him standing on the patio talking to a group of people. He smiled and called, 'Come and meet some of my relatives, Lorna!' When she came closer he put a possessive arm around her and drew her into the circle. Lorna noticed the looks that passed between some of them, particularly the women, and she knew that before long the news that Jason was involved with a Canadian girl would rush like a brush fire through the Peritakis clan.

After a while the group dispersed and Lorna and Jason were left alone. 'My family likes you,' he said with satisfaction, 'I could tell.'

'Well, I like them too,' Lorna said, 'except that there seem to be so many of them. I don't think I'll ever be able to sort them out.'

'Then you had better stay in Crete for a long, long time,' Jason replied softly, slipping his arm from her shoulder to her narrow waist and pulling her closer.

She flushed with pleasure, but did not pursue this delightful prospect. 'Jason, there's something I want to tell you while we're by ourselves,' she said.

'Is it such a secret *kookla mou*?' he teased.

'As a matter of fact it is. No! . . . be serious a minute,' she giggled as he started to nibble at her ear-lobe, 'it's about the dig.' She told him of yesterday's find, and to her surprise his reaction was not one of pleasure. His face grew sombre, and his dark brows drew together in a frown.

'Spanakis did not send this find to the museum last night?' he asked sharply.

'No. I'm to photograph it on Monday, and then it goes to Iraklion. Harvey says he wanted to gloat over it,' she chuckled, 'I guess he can't bear to part with it yet.'

'*Hristo!* Such madness!' Taken aback by his vehemence Lorna stood back and gazed at him through wide blue eyes. 'I must find Spanakis,' he said, moving down the steps. 'It must be put in the safe in my office immediately.' He was so distracted that he nearly knocked down one of the young Athenian men who was coming to ask Lorna for a dance. Jason uttered a stifled oath, and apprehension clutched at Lorna's heart. Were they in for one of his jealous scenes? But her fears were groundless. After a few hurried words in Greek Jason said, 'Do you remember George *kookla mou*?' She nodded. 'He wants to know if you will dance with him.'

'I . . . I don't know Jason . . . is it safe?' she asked with studied meekness.

For a moment Jason's dark mood lifted and he grinned at her boyishly. 'Of course it is, my darling,' he said, 'I am sure George is not in the least dangerous.'

She raised herself on her tip-toes and kissed his lean cheek. 'Bless you, Jason,' she whispered.

He patted her shoulder, then said, 'You must excuse me now, I go to find Professor Spanakis,' and with an absent smile he left them.

Lorna danced with George, and as she had said she would, she told him how things stood between her and Jason, and George wished her happiness, and gallantly told her that he thought Jason was a very lucky man.

Nikos reappeared and claimed her for the next dance. To her surprise he was reasonably sober. He wasn't very talkative, but at least he didn't complain to her about Jason, which was a welcome change.

And then it was time for Ariadne and Kosti to leave for Iraklion. The guests milled around the driveway for a glimpse of the bride in her blue silk suit. And those that had cars piled into them, followed by hopeful would-be passengers.

Lorna saw Jason in earnest conversation with Professor Spanakis. The portly little man nodded several times in agreement, and then he trotted away.

Jason let his gaze wander over the crowd until he saw Lorna. Then he waved and came over to her. 'We will drive to the harbour with my mother,' he said.

She looked at the crush of people pushing themselves into cars and *mikanos*, screaming with laughter and stepping on each other's feet. 'Is everyone going to Iraklion?' she asked. Thinking that if mother and daughter wanted a private farewell they were in for a disappointment.

'Everyone who can get a lift. It is the custom to walk with the newly married pair to see them off. But Iraklion is too far I think.' He guided her towards the chauffered Daimler. Madam Peritakis was already on the back seat, surrounded by various female relatives.

Lorna hung back, suddenly shy. 'I don't want to intrude, Jason,' she said, 'if you're short of room . . .'

Jason's mother rolled down the window another inch and called, 'Jason! You will ride in the front with Manolis, and for Lorna I have saved the jumping seat.'

Suppressing a smile Lorna thanked her hostess and climbed into the car. She caught a glimpse of Maria and Irene. The child was wearing the new white dress Lorna had given her, and had pink ribbons in her hair. Jason went over to them and after a few words he took the little girl's hand and brought her to the car. Settling on to the front seat he put Irene on his lap. 'We have an extra passenger,' he informed the others. 'This young lady expressed a desire to see the bride off on her honeymoon. I thought she should not be disappointed.' Irene smiled at them shyly, then gave her full attention to pretending to drive, making 'engine noises' under her breath all the way to Iraklion.

The adults did not say much during the journey. It had been a long, full day, and Lorna sensed that now that the moment for Ariadne to leave her childhood home had arrived her mother was feeling particularly emotional.

The honeymooners were to cruise the Aegean Islands before starting married life in Athens, and to greet them the yacht was again ablaze with light, and the crew, in pristine white uniforms, stood on deck.

Ariadne, her green eyes suspiciously bright, embraced her mother and her brother. Then she came to Lorna who was standing discreetly apart from the family. She flung her arms around the Canadian girl. 'I do not say "goodbye" to you Lorna,' she said, 'for we are friends, and true friends never really part.'

Lorna smiled. She said, 'Be happy Ariadne ... I know you will be.'

'And you Lorna ... you be happy too,' Ariadne whispered, kissing Lorna's smooth oval cheek. She went to her husband's side and together they walked up the gangplank. It was drawn in and the yacht pulled away. There was a cry of farewell from the shore and

someone threw a shower of rose petals which floated on
the trembling moonlit water for a few moments before
disappearing in the wash.

Jason put one arm around his mother, the other
round Lorna. He murmured something in Greek and
Madam Peritakis smiled wanly and dabbed at her eyes
with a lace-trimmed handkerchief. 'You are right, my
son,' she replied in English, 'we must look to the future.
I will not be sad.' And once they were back in the car
she made a conscious effort at gaiety, and the return
trip was lightened by a steady chirrup of conversation.
Only Irene was silent. The moment the car drove off she
fell into a deep sleep, cuddled on Lorna's lap this time,
her little body as relaxed as a rag doll.

A haze of content floated over Lorna. The little grey
cloud that had hovered over her that morning had long
since disappeared. Jason had been loving towards her in
the presence of his family. And if the cousins looked at
her a trifle warily, at least there was no animosity in
their eyes.

She wondered how her own relations would view the
Peritakis family in general, and Jason in particular, and
she had the feeling they would all get along pretty well.
But even while she thought this she realised that
whether they liked him or not it would not make an
iota of difference to the way *she* felt. She was
committed one hundred per cent, and while it would be
nice to have their approval, nothing they could say or
do could come between her and the man she loved.
Could the same be said for Ariadne? If Madam
Peritakis and Jason had been violently opposed to her
marriage, would she have stood up to them and married
her Kosti no matter what they thought? Perhaps. But it
would not have been typical behaviour for a girl
brought up in Crete. And what about Jason? If his
mother and sister hadn't taken to Lorna so warmly,
would he have shown his affection so openly? Or would
he have hidden his true feelings and merely indulged in

a little surreptitious lovemaking when no one was around?

It's when the cultural differences start to hurt you that things become impossible, Lorna thought, her new-found contentment fading a little. And you never know when that's going to happen. You have to be constantly on your guard.

Suddenly the sound of the Greek conversation going on softly around her made her feel unbearably alien, and for a moment the magic of Crete turned to black magic. She felt alone, and a little frightened. The moment passed as swiftly as it had materialised, like a pattern in a kaleidoscope. But the dim memory of that pattern stayed at the edge of her consciousness like a dull toothache that refused to go away.

So immersed was she in this troubled reverie that she hardly noticed when the car drew up at the front of the villa. And when Jason opened the door and said, 'Let me take Irene. She will be too heavy for you,' she was startled. He chuckled softly. 'Perhaps I should carry both of you,' he said as he gently took the sleeping child in his arms, 'you seem as tired as she is.' And she realised then that she was indeed bone-weary.

She walked with Jason to where Maria sat with a group of village women. Jason said something in rapid Greek, then waved away a protest of Maria's. Lorna was too sleepy to make out the words, but when they all returned to the waiting Daimler she understood that Maria and her daughter were to be driven home.

Maria kissed Lorna good night and sat in the back of the big car while Jason carefully laid Irene on her lap. He was just closing the door when they heard a strangled shout, and Professor Spanakis ran up from the direction of the orange groves. He had obviously been running for some time, for when he reached them he had to struggle to catch his breath. He finally gasped out something in Greek.

The blood seemed to drain out of Jason's face, and his hands clenched so hard his knuckles turned white.

'What is it?' Lorna cried. 'What's happened?'

He looked at her and she was shocked to see his face so bleached of colour. 'What is it?' she repeated, clutching at his arm. He felt as rigid as iron.

'The little head,' he said harshly, 'the little head has disappeared.'

CHAPTER NINE

LORNA stared at him in disbelief. 'Disappeared! I ... I don't understand.'

'It is another theft, Lorna,' the Professor said. With a shaking hand he removed his glasses and wiped his forehead. 'The lock had been broken on the door of the shed.'

'Was anything else taken?' Lorna asked.

The plump Greek shook his head. 'No. Only the terracotta ... in any case the rest of the finds were fragments only, worth little compared to the head.' He replaced his glasses and turned to Jason. 'I blame myself entirely,' he said brokenly, 'I should have sent it *immediately* to Iraklion. But I thought it would be safe since it is the weekend and the site is deserted. I shall never forgive myself. Never.' The poor man seemed on the brink of tears.

Jason put a comforting arm across his shoulders and murmured something in his own tongue, but when the older man still shook his head despondently he became businesslike and took charge. 'First we must phone the police,' he said. 'Lorna, will you help the Professor into the house and pour him a glass of brandy.' Professor Spanakis started to protest, but when Jason paid not the slightest attention he subsided like a kettle coming off the boil.

Lorna led him into the drawing room while Jason went to his office to phone. She poured a generous slug of Metaxa brandy into a snifter and handed it to her boss, who in spite of his former protests took it gratefully.

'I'm sure the police will soon find the culprit,' she reassured him, 'try not to worry too much.'

154

'Even if they do,' he said lugubriously, 'it is doubtful they will find either the head or the seal stones. Doubtless the thief has already arranged to sell them on the black market. It is dreadful, dreadful! And I blame myself for this new loss entirely. I should have put the terracotta in a safe place, not left it lying around so conveniently for the robber.'

Since Lorna was inclined to agree with this she maintained a discreet silence, and no more was said until Jason returned.

He had changed out of his Cretan costume and put on worn jeans and faded blue cotton shirt. 'The police will be here within the hour,' he told them. 'They wish to interview all those involved with the dig right away.' He turned to Lorna and the laughing debonair man who had teased and kissed her was gone. In his place was a man used to giving orders, and having them instantly obeyed. 'Would you ask your colleagues to come in here, please, Lorna? Try not to let anyone else know that anything is wrong. There is no need to broadcast the news of this fresh robbery. It will be common knowledge soon enough, God knows, but I would prefer it if Ariadne's wedding day was left unsullied for as long as possible.'

He looked haunted, gaunt. While she sympathised with his distress, she couldn't help feeling that he seemed to be taking it very personally. After all, even though it was on his land, it wasn't *his* terracotta that had been stolen. He looked as bereft as if he had been robbed of all he owned.

'Send them here to the drawing room please,' he ordered sharply.

She said she would and, her weariness forgotten, she went out into the garden to round up the archaeological team. She managed to field their questions skilfully, and within half-an-hour they were all gathered in the brightly lit room. Jason had drawn the silk blinds, and already the air was electric with tension. Professor

Spanakis seemed to have regained some of his usual composure, and sat apart at a small rosewood table. But Jason hovered at the far end of the room, jumpy as a thoroughbred racehorse at the starting post. His fine eyes kept glancing at the door to scan each new arrival. When Nikos came in it looked as if Jason was about to say something to his cousin, but he seemed to think better of it, and contented himself with a piercing gaze that the young man returned nonchalantly.

Nikos had surprised her again. She had expected him to be difficult, but he had merely nodded when she asked him to show himself in the drawing room. He didn't even ask why he was being summoned. And he seemed to be stone cold sober. Maybe he's turning over a new leaf, she thought, and she wondered if that was why Jason looked at him so speculatively.

When they had all found seats and were uneasily waiting for some explanation, Jason asked Professor Spanakis to delay his announcement for a few minutes. 'I think it only right that I ask my mother to be present,' he said. 'If you will excuse me I will fetch her.'

There was a shuffling of feet and Harvey leaned over to Lorna. 'Am I right in guessing that our local crook has struck again?' he whispered.

'You'll find out soon enough,' Lorna whispered back, earning a look of disapproval from the Professor.

Jason came back with his mother. She gave a sympathetic glance towards Professor Spanakis before seating herself in a chair at the back of the room. The Professor then told the group what had occurred. As before, he spoke first in Greek, and then in English. He made no attempt to gloss over his own negligence in the affair, and Lorna's heart went out to him.

There was a frozen silence when he had finished. 'This time I offer no "deal" to the perpetrator of the crime,' he added. 'At any minute now the authorities will arrive, and believe me I shall do all in my power to assist them to apprehend the culprit.' He looked at the assembled field-workers with severity, before re-seating himself beside the little table.

Madam Peritakis left them, promising to arrange for coffee to be sent in. She was pale, and her usually firm voice trembled, and Lorna wondered again why the Peritakis family seemed so personally overwhelmed by this event. It must be the Cretan temperament at work again. All the same it must be dreadfully wearing, she thought, to get so emotionally caught up in things.

They had just been served their coffee when the police arrived. Jason went to meet the inspector in the hall, and after a hurried consultation it was arranged that the interviews would be conducted in the study. Harvey was the first to be called in.

Susan came and sat beside her friend. 'Isn't this the pits?' she said softly. 'I personally would like to kick whoever did it in his rear-end.'

'I'll lend you my hiking boots for the job,' Lorna offered, draining her cup and replacing it on one of the trays. 'It's a lousy ending to a lovely day.'

'Jason looks wiped out.' Susan nodded her curly head in his direction.

'Yes he does,' Lorna agreed. A wave of tenderness swept over her at the sight of his drawn face. She would have given anything to be alone with him now. To take that tired, proud head and draw it down to her breast, and stroke his dark hair and comfort him. Darling, darling Jason, I love you so much, she thought. At that moment he glanced up at her and for a second the shadows left his eyes and the ghost of a smile touched his mouth.

Nikos ambled over to the coffee tray and helped himself to another cup. Whatever strain the other members of the Peritakis family suffered it certainly wasn't being shared by him. He seemed positively chipper. He was full of repressed glee, like a man who had just heard a good joke and can't wait to share it. 'When the police have gone we will drink much brandy and dance until the morning. *Ne?*' he said.

'I do not think we will be in the mood,' said Jason, crossing to him.

Nikos looked at him derisively. 'Ah! You must not be depressed. One little statue! Pooh!' He made a dismissive gesture. 'The earth is full of such treasures. For that one you will find a hundred more, I promise you.'

'I don't think that's quite the point,' Lorna said, trying to be diplomatic.

Susan, not trying to be diplomatic at all said, 'Belt up, Nikos!' And with a shrug he returned to his chair.

Jason followed him. 'You are not upset, Nikos?' he asked. 'You are not upset by this crime?'

For the first time that evening Nikos's good humour seemed to fade a little. 'Upset! For what reason should I be? It has nothing to do with me,' he blustered.

'It has to do with all of us,' Jason said levelly. 'As a Cretan you should know that such a theft reflects on the whole village. We are all tainted by it.'

'That kind of talk is based on superstition,' said Nikos. 'I am a modern man. I do not listen to such things.'

'Perhaps you should listen, Nikos,' Jason said to him softly, 'it might remind you of your heritage.' He stayed looking down at his cousin who refused to return his gaze, but kept staring down into his coffee cup.

Harvey returned from his interview and now it was Lorna's turn. Since she could account for her movements for the entire day the questioning did not take long, but afterwards her dark-room was searched from top to bottom.

Jason came and stood by her side while this was going on. 'I am sorry *kookla mou*,' he said.

'It's not your fault, darling,' she smiled up at him.

He lightly traced the circles of fatigue under her eyes. 'You are exhausted *kookla mou*,' he whispered, 'the moment they are finished here you will go to bed.'

'That doesn't seem very fair to the others,' she said. But he was firm.

'Do not argue with me, Lorna. I do not want you to become ill on top of everything else. Please do as I say.' And she was so happy that he was taking charge and looking after her, that she agreed without another murmur.

The two policemen asked her to unlock her box of personal photographs. The ones she planned to use for her book. She lifted out the pictures so the box could be examined, and Jason took the pile of photos from her and started to look at them. After carefully studying a group she was particularly pleased with—a series of shots of peasants' hands, gnarled and roughened with work—he looked at her with new respect.

'Now I begin to understand why your work is so important to you, Lorna.' He shuffled through a few more of the pictures, ones showing Irene at play while her mother worked at her spinning, shepherds gossiping under the olive trees, the ever-present, numinous mountains. 'You are an artist,' he said finally. 'You have captured the true spirit of my village.'

The policemen indicated that they had finished, and after politely bidding them both good night they left the dark-room. Lorna put her photographs back in their box, locked it, and wearily pushed her hair away from her face. She was suddenly so tired that even Jason's approval of her work failed to rouse her to any enthusiasm. When she turned to leave she stumbled. Jason was instantly at her side, his strong arms around her, half lifting her out into the night.

Standing under the purple blossoms of the Chaste Tree he held her close and she sighed and relaxed against him. The crisp hair on his chest brushed her cheek. As she snuggled closer she could smell the warm, male scent of him, and a faint tremor of desire stirred in her.

He leaned his chin on the top of her silky head. 'I wish that I could carry you to my bed and lull you to

sleep in my arms *agapi mou*,' he murmured, and she
gave a contented little grunt and burrowed closer.

He chuckled and lightly kissed her hair before
pushing her gently away from him. 'Come! I will take
you to your room. You are nearly asleep standing up.'

At her door he kissed her swiftly. Once on the mouth,
and on each eye-lid. 'Go straight to sleep and dream of
me,' he ordered before leaving her.

That reminded her of the sugared almond in the
pocket of her dress. She put it under her pillow, but she
didn't dream at all. Or if she did she was too tired to
remember.

The following day was spent quietly. There were still
visitors, people from other villages who came to drink a
glass of wine and toast the departed bridal pair. But
apart from these occasional cheering interruptions there
was a feeling of let-down, a reaction both to the
excitement of the the previous day, and to the discovery
of the missing terracotta.

Lorna hardly saw Jason. He spent long hours
closeted in his study with either Professor Spanakis or
the chief of police, and when he did emerge he was so
abstracted he really might not have been with her at all.
She began to feel rather neglected and shut out. Both he
and his mother were still sunk in gloom over the whole
business, and Lorna's sympathy began to wear a bit
thin. No one would deny that it was a dreadful thing
for an historical site to be plundered, but one must have
a sense of proportion. As far as Lorna was concerned
Madam Peritakis and Jason were carrying things a little
too far. She tried dispensing some astringent Canadian
common sense, and even attempted to crack a joke or
two, but these efforts met with such stony looks from
both mother and son that she gave up in disgust.

After lunch, when Jason had joined them to bid
farewell to a departing guest, he told her that he had
invited Susan and Harvey to spend the afternoon and
evening at the villa. 'It will be company for you, Lorna,'

he said, 'while I deal with this other matter.'

'Do you mean to tell me you're going to spend the rest of the day with Professor Spanakis at your private wake?' she asked abruptly.

'Believe me I would prefer to spend the time with you, Lorna, but under the circumstances it is not possible.' He looked at her sternly, as a loving father looks at a recalcitrant child, and this succeeded in irritating her further.

'What *circumstances*?' she demanded.

'I should not have to explain that since this crime has been committed on Peritakis land we are directly involved . . . and there is more . . .' He hesitated, as if deciding whether or not to tell her something important.

'I still can't see why you have to make it such a . . . such a tragedy,' she protested.

'You seem to forget that to a Cretan, theft is the worst of all crimes,' he said in a flint-hard voice. 'The thief not only brings dishonour on himself, but on his family and the community as well. Please try to understand this. It may help to curb your vexation.'

'I'm not vexed,' she replied, sounding very vexed indeed, 'it's just that I don't see that . . . that carrying *on* like this solves anything. It seems self-indulgent if you want my opinion.'

'I do not!' he said, his lips thin with anger.

'Fine! Go back to your wake then. I'll go for a swim before the others come.' She left him hurriedly, thinking, There we go again! More cultural barriers. And when she changed into her black bikini she had to bite her lip to stop the angry tears spilling from her eyes.

She spent the afternoon lazing round the pool with Susan and Harvey. Outwardly she appeared quite cheerful. Inside she was tied in knots. She realised that she was being unfair, but she seemed incapable of controlling her mounting resentment, which she knew stemmed from insecurity. But knowing the source didn't prevent her from feeling that horrible sensation of being a stranger in Jason's world. As the afternoon passed her voice and laugh grew shrill with the effort of maintaining the illusion of happiness, and by the time Jason joined them for a swim before dinner she had worked herself into a state where she felt at odds with everything around her. Even watching Jason's lithe body cutting effortlessly through the water caused her pain. His very attractiveness seemed to set him apart from her. Her forced laughter stilled, and she became silent. Looking at her lover with grave and troubled eyes.

For his part Jason was politely attentive—but wary with her—which she was beginning to discover was his way when she attacked him. And though the other two were no doubt unaware that anything was wrong, she felt as if a wide chasm had opened up between Jason and herself. A horrible empty space that would never be bridged.

When she went upstairs to dress for dinner Susan came too. After she had duly admired Lorna's room she changed back into her dress and repaired her make-up. 'Isn't it great that the boys get on so well?' she said.

Lorna paused in the act of putting on her emerald green silk dress. 'Boys?'

'Harvey and Jason. They really do seem to hit it off.'

'Oh! Yes. Yes they do.' She would never in a million years have thought of Jason as a 'boy'.

Susan powdered the end of her tip-tilted nose. 'It's hard to think of Jason and Nikos as coming from the same family, isn't it?' she ventured.

'What brought that on?' asked Lorna, settling the green silk on her hips. She wasn't at all sure that she wanted to go on discussing the Peritakis family, she felt too upset. But there seemed to be no way of stopping Susan.

'I was just thinking ... when he left the taverna to

come here Nikos was sitting in the garden ... getting plastered! He was knocking back the raki as if there was no tomorrow!'

'I guess he's making up for yesterday,' Lorna said, 'he certainly stayed remarkably sober at the reception. I was surprised.'

'He was probably scared to death of Jason. I don't imagine he'd stand for that kind of behaviour at his sister's wedding. I should think your Jason could be pretty scary when he gets mad.'

'Pretty scary ... yes,' Lorna admitted. 'What about Harvey? Does he have a temper?' As she had hoped this ploy released a rapturous flood of anecdotes concerning Harvey's good nature and general saintliness and Jason was forgotten.

They ate in the dining room with Jason and Madam Peritakis. The food was simple and good, but the general atmosphere was a little *triste*. Over coffee on the patio Jason and Harvey got into an involved discussion about the theory of Santorini being the lost island of Atlantis, while the three women, in the fashion of all Greek gatherings, drew a little apart from the men. This was yet another thorn in Lorna's side. She stared unseeingly out at the scented night, the stars hung so low and clear they reminded her of the crystal drops on the chandelier in the dining room.

'You are so quiet, Lorna,' Madam Peritakis remarked. 'Do you not feel well, child?'

'I do have a bit of a headache,' Lorna said, although heart-ache would have been nearer the truth.

'Lorna! Why didn't you *say* something?' Susan protested. 'You must be longing to lie down.'

Harvey checked his watch. 'It's time we went anyway,' he said. 'Tomorrow's a working day after all, and we don't want to overstay our welcome.'

Jason and Lorna walked their guests to the jeep Harvey had borrowed from the dig.

'It's been a great day,' Harvey said, shaking Jason's

hand fervently, 'thanks a million, Jason.'

'It has been a pleasure for me,' Jason replied, helping Susan, who was experiencing difficulty climbing into the passenger seat.

'Whew! These things ought to come equipped with a lift,' she puffed when she was finally settled. ''Night Jason. Take care of that headache, Lorna!' She gave a final wave and the jeep roared away.

When the tail-lights had disappeared Jason put his hands on Lorna's shoulders and stared intently into her face. In the dark his eyes seemed to glow like a mountain cat's. She had the distinct feeling that those clear eyes could see straight into her heart and not be taken in by any defences she might use to fool him.

'How is your headache now?' he asked.

'Okay . . . better.' She turned her head to avoid that penetrating gaze.

'But you are still angry with me, *ne*?'

'Not angry,' she protested. Meeting his relentless stare again she added more truthfully, 'Well . . . not any more. Just tired.'

And worried about us and the yawning pit that stretches between us, she might have added, but didn't.

He put his arms around her and drew her close. She didn't resist—how could she, when even his lightest touch made her blood stir with delight.

'I must ask you to be understanding, *kookla mou*,' he murmured, 'I have worries that you cannot share . . .'

'Why don't you try me,' she cut in.

'. . . Worries that you cannot share at this moment,' he repeated.

'I don't much enjoy being excluded like this,' she said. 'It doesn't make me feel particularly welcome in your life.'

He tilted her face to look up at him but she turned her eyes away. 'That is nonsense, Lorna,' he said patiently. 'I love you with all my heart, believe me.'

'But not enough to share your worries with me,' she insisted obstinately.

'Hristo!' he exclaimed in a burst of irritation, 'you are as stubborn as one of the village mules.'

'Thank you very much!' She tried to pull herself out of his arms but he still held her tightly.

'I tell you it is not in my power to share this ... anxiety ... with you at this time.'

'Why not? Because I'm a woman? Is that it?' She had no idea what had made her say that. But this latest slight—imagined or not—was the final straw. Her usual control had deserted her.

'It has nothing to do with your sex. Do not be idiotic,' Jason snapped. His fingers dug into her upper arms. 'This is not a question of male chauvinism ...'

'Isn't it?' she cried wildly. 'I would have thought we'd had a pretty good display of chauvinism all day as a matter of fact.'

'What do you mean by that?' he demanded.

'Well ... just generally shutting me out. Patting me on the head from time to time to keep me sweet. Seeing that I have chums to play with ... That sort of thing. While you get on with the grown-up *male* world without me.'

Stop it! Stop it! she silently commanded herself, but she was on a runaway emotional train, and could not apply the brakes.

Slowly he let go of her arms and she made a great show of rubbing them, as if he had hurt her. 'If I did pat you to keep you sweet I failed dismally,' he said.

His face suddenly looked so drawn that her heart twisted with pain. Her instinct was to throw herself back into his arms, and weep and tell him that she loved him so much that the mere *thought* that he couldn't share things with her drove her to behave like a spoilt brat. But as usual her pride prevented her, and she merely muttered, 'Even over coffee you talked exclusively to Harvey.'

He gave an exasperated sigh. 'I would point out, Lorna, that you were unusually silent all evening. If you had wanted to join in the conversation you had only to open your mouth. I now realise that you were sulking.'

'I don't like segregated conversations,' she repeated wilfully.

'Neither do I. Nor do I like sulky women.' There was a silence with Lorna broke.

'We seem to have reached an impasse,' she said tremulously. All her anger had evaporated and now she was filled with apprehension.

When he spoke again his voice sounded strangely flat. 'Perhaps it would be best if we saw less of each other, Lorna . . . during the next few days,' he said.

'That's going to be difficult, isn't it? I mean, we are living under the same roof.' Her own voice sounded steady, which she found remarkable, since her heart had dropped like a stone.

'You managed it once before.' He gave her a wintry smile.

'All that rushing about! I don't think I've the energy for it any more.' She tried to smile back, but her lips felt stiff.

'I shall be away a great deal of the time,' he said. 'And when this . . . this worry is resolved . . .'

'The one you refuse to share with me . . .'

'The one I *cannot* share with you . . . we will have a talk.'

'Why not have a talk now?' She laid her hand on his arm and he lifted it off. The rebuff was gentle, but if he'd struck her he couldn't have hurt her more.

'Now is not the time.' His jaw was set like granite.

'Well, in that case I'll get to bed.' She swallowed a lump in her throat the size of a cannon-ball. 'Good night, Jason.' Kiss me! Kiss me! she screamed silently at him, but it didn't work, and he merely muttered, '*Kalinihta*, Lorna,' and went into the night.

She managed to control her tears until she had reached the sanctuary of her bedroom. Then the storm broke! She flung herself down on the satin bedspread and cried as she had never cried before. When at last she stumbled into the bathroom to splash cold water on to her tear-blotched face she was exhausted. The alienation she felt before was nothing to the vast gulf that existed now. A gulf of her own making. How could she have behaved so stupidly? Again and again she berated herself as she lay tossing and turning on her bed through the long night.

She was determined about one thing, however; this time she would not try to avoid Jason. Even though the very thought of facing him was like a knife in her side, the thought of not seeing him was worse. Like a death. Better the knife than that!

But in the morning the breakfast table on the patio was deserted, and although she spent as long as she reasonably could over a cup of coffee (she couldn't eat a thing, it would have choked her), there was no sign of him.

And her work was no help to her this time. She was constantly aware that she was on Jason's land. Every stone and dusty blade of grass reminded her of him, and she spent a good deal of the morning with one part of her listening for the sound of his horse's hooves . . . or the sound of his voice calling her name. But he never came.

During the lunch break she walked back to the villa. She had decided to work for the rest of the day in her dark-room . . . maybe she would see Jason and talk to him. She would throw herself on his mercy, tell him how miserable she was, how idiotic she had been.

The villa was silent when she got there. It was the siesta hour. But on her way up to her room to wash and change out of her shorts she met Madam Peritakis, wearing a large hat and carrying a handbag.

'Lorna, what are you doing back here in the daytime?' she asked.

Lorna explained that she intended to work in the dark-room, enlarging some prints. Madam Peritakis looked at her carefully and said, 'You look very tired, my dear. You would be better to have a siesta I think.'

Lorna smiled wanly. 'I don't seem to have the knack for sleeping at the moment, so I might as well work.' She added with elaborate casualness, 'Is Jason anywhere around?'

Madam Peritakis's expressive face grew cautious. 'Jason is out on . . . on business. He will not be home until evening.'

'Oh!'

The bleakness Lorna felt on receiving this information must have been apparent, for the older woman said kindly, 'I think you should take the afternoon off, my dear. If you will not take a siesta, perhaps you should go to the beach . . . make a break in your routine. I myself am going to Iraklion to a committee meeting. And while Iraklion is not the ideal place for a relaxing afternoon there are many attractive beaches close by. After he has taken me to my meeting, Manolis could drive you to one.'

Lorna hesitated for a moment, but the thought of lying on a silvery beach compared to an afternoon trying to work and not think of Jason was irresistible.

'What a great idea!' she said. 'Give me a couple of minutes to change and I'll be with you.'

She raced upstairs thinking that if Jason was out there was no sense moping around the house. She could easily catch up with her work later. Meantime she would have a swim and decide what she was going to say to him when she saw him. To mentally prepare herself, so there would be no more misunderstandings.

They were driven to Iraklion in the black sedan, sitting together in the back seat like Royalty. Madam Peritakis always seemed to travel this way, and Lorna asked her if she knew how to drive.

'Alas! No.' The older woman shook her head, which

set the brim of her hat nodding. 'In my day it was not usual for a woman to drive. Now of course that has changed. Ariadne is a splendid driver, for instance. And you, Lorna? Do you drive also?'

'I have since I was seventeen. I love it.'

'Then you must use Ariadne's car while you are here. Kosti has bought her a new one for her life in Athens. You have the appropriate documents, I assume?'

'Oh! Sure.' She thought for a moment. 'But if there's a car to spare . . . I mean maybe Nikos might like to use it.' She remembered his wistful remarks about cars.

'It is not possible for Nikos to use Ariadne's car,' Madam Peritakis said firmly.

'It's just that I know he misses not having a car . . . he's told me so . . . I mean . . . he is part of the family,' she explained, hoping Jason's mother wouldn't think she was being ungracious.

Madam Peritakis stared straight ahead. 'Did Nikos tell you *why* he has no vehicle?' she asked.

'Well . . . no. I just assumed he couldn't afford one.'

'Nikos is not allowed to drive by law. His driver's licence has been . . . how do you call it? Taken from him.'

'Revoked?'

'Yes . . . that is the word. Because of the many accidents he had while under the influence of wine.'

'Oh! . . . I'm sorry . . .' She wasn't quite sure what else to say.

'I, too, am sorry, Lorna,' Madam Peritakis said softly. 'My heart is sad for my nephew, but we seem unable to help him. Do you know anything of his history?' When Lorna shook her head she continued, 'Nikos was most unfortunate in his parents. His father, my brother-in-law, was an unfeeling man. Not cruel you understand, but uninterested in his young son. He died when Nikos was quite small and his mother brought him up . . . disastrously.' She took a bottle of cologne from her handbag and lightly dabbed the insides of her wrists while she talked. 'Nikos's mother was one of the silliest women I have ever known,' she said reflectively, 'She *adored* her son and gave in to his every whim. He disliked school—so she removed him from it. She hired tutors, but if they exercised any discipline they were dismissed. She treated Nikos like an eighteenth-century prince. Anything he wanted she bought for him.

'He was nineteen when she died, and by then it was too late. He was ruined, and through no fault of his own. My husband tried to help by seeing that his share of the Peritakis money was not left to him outright— since he would undoubtedly squander it—but put in trust and given to him in the form of an allowance. A safeguard Nikos bitterly resents.' She replaced the cap on the cologne bottle. 'Children should not be left to grow like weeds,' she said, 'they need guidance and discipline in order to become responsible adults. Poor Nikos never received an ounce of help from his parents. Is it any wonder that now he is a bitter, drunken man . . . a disgrace to the name of Peritakis.' Her eyes filled with sudden tears and then she said quietly, so that Lorna could scarcely hear her, 'And now? *Mou Theos!* Who knows where it will end?'

'You mustn't blame yourself,' Lorna comforted, 'you and your husband . . . I'm sure you did all you could.'

'But the shame . . . It is for all of us.' She dabbed at her eyes with a handkerchief, then seemed to remember her duties as a hostess and pulled herself together. 'Ah! I believe I am still overwrought from the wedding.' She smiled wryly. 'Please to forgive a foolish old woman.'

'I don't think of you as a foolish old woman, believe me, Madam,' Lorna said, venturing to squeeze her beringed hand. 'There's nothing to forgive. I'm flattered that you confided in me.'

They were now driving through the outskirts of Iraklion, and Madam Peritakis smoothed her silk dress and straightened her hat in order to be tidy for her meeting. When they reached her destination she kissed Lorna warmly on the cheek and said, 'Try and relax this afternoon my dear, and get rid of those shadows round your pretty eyes.'

For a moment Lorna wanted to fling herself in the older woman's arms, and tell her of her quarrel with Jason, and how she longed to put it right, but she restrained herself. 'I'll have a good swim,' was all she said, 'that always helps me to relax.'

'Why not let Manolis drive you to Rethimnon? There is time. And the beach there is most pleasant,' Madam Peritakis suggested when she had been helped by the chauffeur from the car. Lorna agreed to this, and her hostess gave Manolis his orders in rapid Greek, and with a wave to Lorna went to keep her appointment.

They drove to the sleepy port town of Rethimnon on the new road, through the magnificent gaunt hills that line the coast. To their right lay the sea like a sheet of burning metal in the sun. Oleanders flowered profusely in the dry stream beds, and patches of vivid wild geraniums flared with colour in the ditches.

When they reached Rethimnon Manolis stopped at the bus station and after Lorna had discovered that there were plenty of buses back to the village, she dismissed him, assuring him she would have no difficulty finding her own way home. Then she set out to explore the town.

She found it a gentle, delicate place, dilapidated certainly, but full of charm. She explored the sleepy walls of the huge Venetian fortress that enclosed thistles and pines, and ruined official buildings. Memories of a citadel that was once alive and bustling. Then she made her way to the curved and sandy beach, protected east and west by harbour moles. It was not particularly crowded, and she had a long and delicious swim in the warm water without the feeling of being in a resort at all. She sunbathed for a while, then pulled on her cotton sundress and went in search of iced coffee and one of the town's renowned Levantine pastries.

She discovered that some of the best patisseries were
along the front, and seating herself at a table at one of
the cafés she slowly and sensuously enjoyed a honey-
dripping confection. Then she sat, looking at the waves
frilling along the beach like an uneven hem of lace, and
in her imagination she rehearsed what she would say to
Jason.

She would promise that never again would she let her
pride come between them. She would explain that her
fear of losing him drove her to act foolishly, and she
would vow in future to tell him when she was racked
with doubt, so that a small uncertainty would not have
a chance to grow into a monster. And Jason would
understand. He would take her in his arms and comfort
her. He would forgive her, and love her, and all would
be well.

She was feeling almost happy when she left the front
and made her way through the maze of little streets that
led to the bus station. She noticed that many of the
houses and shops had stone-built Venetian doorways,
and peering inside she could sometimes see stone arches
holding up the ceilings, and there were a great number
of Turkish-style balconies here too, leaning out over the
streets, their ancient woodwork pale and delicate.

She came across a little square, the centre planted
with eucalyptus and a bank of oleanders and shrubs. At
one end stood a mosque with a prettily fluted minaret.
At the other end was a little fountain. It was a cool
place with columns and Corinthian capitals. She paused
for a minute before deciding which alley she would take
on the upward climb.

She chose one that had some rather seedy shops in it,
and within a few seconds she realised that the graceful
character of the town had changed. Now she was in a
distinctly disreputable district. Run down and sleazy,
but with some fascinating, if shabby, architecture,
nevertheless. She made a mental note to ask Jason to

bring her here so she could take some pictures, the contrasts were terrific. Then at that moment she saw a pair of familiar wide shoulders lurking in a doorway.

She stopped dead in her tracks and called, 'Jason!' in a clear, high-pitched voice, and he started as if he had been jolted by an electric charge. 'Jason!' she cried again, and ran towards him, thinking what an extraordinary coincidence it was that he should happen to be in Rethimnon too, and appear like that, just when she was thinking of him. Now she wouldn't have to wait until evening for their reconciliation. They could probably travel back to the village together, too.

When she got closer she noticed that his eyes were wide with disbelief. He looked furtively up and down the grubby alley and then said her name in a voice so hard and tense she scarcely recognised it.

'What do you do here?' he said with such ferocity she flinched.

'I . . . I'm on my way to the bus station,' she faltered, 'I've . . . I've been swimming.'

He looked at her suspiciously. 'Do you plan to meet someone here?'

'Of course not,' she protested. 'I told you . . . I went swimming . . . but I'm so happy to run into you like this . . . I wanted to . . .'

His hand shot out and gripped her shoulder, and he pushed her, brutally it seemed to her, up the dirty narrow street. 'Get away, Lorna!' he hissed. 'Get away from here.'

Out of the bright nightmare she heard herself say, 'Jason! Listen!'

But he ignored her and gave her another push. '*Hristo!* Will you get away from here!' He dropped his hand from her shoulder and stood over her, his face contorted with an emotion she was unable to recognise.

With a pathetic attempt at dignity she deliberately re-fastened the strings of her beach-bag before putting it over her shoulder. Then she left him without another word. When she had walked a few steps she turned to look back, hoping dimly that it was all a hideous mistake, and that he would now come running after her.

But he had returned to his post in the doorway and wasn't even looking in her direction.

CHAPTER TEN

LORNA did not remember the journey back to the village, for her pain was so intense it acted like a narcotic. She sat motionless in the bus, while all around her people jostled and shouted greetings to each other over the sound of the Greek dance music that blasted out of the driver's tape-deck. Dry-eyed she stared ahead, taking as little notice of the hubbub as a rock buffeted by a turbulent sea.

When they reached their destination she phoned the villa from Vasily's stuffy little office to say she would not be coming back that night. She thought the maid she spoke to said that neither the *Kiria* nor the *Kirios* would be home until late, but she was too anguished to take it in. It didn't matter anyway. He had told her to 'get away', and she would not spend another night under his roof.

She plodded upstairs to Susan's room, putting one foot automatically in front of the other. She had discovered that if she made every movement very deliberately, paying strict attention to the minutest details ... such as opening and closing her purse, or dialling the numbers on the phone ... she could hang on to her self-control. By focusing all her attention on these instinctive actions the floodgates of emotion were kept closed.

To her relief Susan was out, but her room-mate, a rather phlegmatic British girl, was there and lent Lorna the sleeping-bag she asked for without a moment's hesitation. Lorna put its rolled bulk under her arm and set off for Maria's little house.

Her self-control wobbled perilously when Irene shot out of the house to greet her. The touch of those thin

175

arms hugging her waist made her falter for a minute, but she blinked hard and forced her lips into the semblance of a smile.

She managed to summon enough Greek to ask if she could stay overnight, and although Maria looked puzzled she didn't ask any awkward questions. Lorna hoped she might think that there had been an influx of visitors at the villa and her room was needed, although that seemed an unlikely explanation.

The books were brought out and Lorna was given her Greek lesson, but she was a poor pupil this evening and Maria cut the lesson short. A half loaf of bread was produced, and some cheese, and for politeness' sake Lorna forced herself to eat some, but it was hard to swallow, for her throat felt as if she wore an iron collar round it, and she was relieved that Maria did not press her to take more.

When their meagre supper had been cleared away, and a shade of violet twilight tinted the evening, they went to bed. The sleeping-bag was laid on the floor of Irene's room, and once that young lady had been persuaded to crawl out of it and into her own little bed, they settled down for the night.

Lorna was convinced she wouldn't sleep a wink, for in spite of the deliberation of her movements, her mind was racing along on two levels. One to deal with the hurt Jason had dealt her, and the other to decide what to do about her immediate future.

The first thing she had to do was to move out of the villa. She had no idea where she would go, there was no room for her at the taverna, and she couldn't impose on Maria indefinitely. But something would have to be worked out. Then she remembered the dark-room! That would have to stay where it was. And that meant she would have to keep going up to Jason's house all the time . . . and she couldn't bear that. And neither presumably could he! Hadn't he told her . . . brutally . . . 'get away from here'. Well, she would do what he commanded. Tomorrow she would give in her notice to Professor Spanakis and leave. She would plead illness, or a sudden emergency at home. She would leave the dig. Leave Crete. Drop the projected book, and fly home to Canada to lick her wounds. There she would pick up the shattered pieces of her life.

This train of thought brought the scalding tears to her eyes, but with a monumental effort she controlled them, staring hard into the dark and willing herself not to give way. Time enough for tears when she was back home. A whole lifetime.

She slept after a while. That same self-control that kept despair at bay also worked to induce sleep. She woke at dawn with a blind sense of loss and the echo of a dream where Jason had again thrust her away from him, and she knew that in spite of her iron will this kind of awakening would be habitual until the pain had dulled.

Hastily she dressed and washed at the stone sink. She forced herself to eat a rusk and drink a glass of water, then she made for the taverna. She would drink a cup of coffee before tackling Professor Spanakis and handing in her notice. For with the daylight she was more convinced than ever that it was impossible to stay in the same *country*, let alone the same village, as Jason.

As luck would have it the Professor's assistant, a pleasant middle-aged Greek named Katerina, was sitting under the plane tree having her breakfast. She was alone, and after fetching herself a cup of coffee from the kitchen Lorna joined her.

She explained that she had had some bad news ... which in a way was the truth since Jason's sudden hatred was the worst sort of news in the world ... and that she would have to leave immediately. She gave Katerina the name of a photographer she knew of in Iraklion that she thought would replace her, and soothed her conscience with the knowledge that at least she wasn't leaving them in the lurch.

Katerina said how sorry they would be to lose Lorna, but she didn't try to persuade her to stay. One look at the Canadian girl's clenched face was enough to convince her that something disastrous had occurred.

'Do you wish to make the arrangements to leave this morning?' Katerina asked, and numbly Lorna said she did. 'Then I will tell you the news Professor Spanakis intends to announce to the team when they assemble on the site,' she said, 'you will want to know I am sure. Perhaps it will bring a little pleasure into your day.'

Lorna was so ferociously unhappy she doubted anything could give her pleasure, but out of politeness she tried to look interested.

'You will be glad to learn that the seal stones *and* the terracotta head have been recovered, and the culprit has been apprehended.' She glowed triumphantly. 'Is that not splendid news?'

'It certainly is,' Lorna agreed. 'Who was the thief?'

The woman's face clouded. 'That is not such good news,' she said, 'for it brings sorrow to the family who have been so kind to us.'

Instantly alert Lorna asked, 'You mean ... the Peritakis family?'

Katerina nodded. 'The thief was Nikos Peritakis.'

The moment Katerina had uttered his name Lorna wondered how she could have been so blind. Why! he must have been disposing of the seal stones the weekend of Kosti's party. *That* was why he never made it! She remembered him on the Monday morning, hung-over and unshaven, waving his drachma-stuffed wallet at her. Boasting that he had money now. How could she have been so *dim*? But her attention had been focused on Jason and the problems of love. The puzzle of the missing seal stones was the last thing on her mind.

Well, that riddle had been solved, and she was relieved the stolen artifacts were recovered. But what a blow for Jason and his mother. Her heart ached, not only for herself, but for them too. She would have given anything to have been able to comfort Jason. Try to make him see that she understood and sympathised. But she was sure any attempt at consolation on her part would not be welcome, and that the sooner she left the island—and his life—the happier he would be.

With a heart as heavy as an iron bar she left Katerina and walked through the orange grove to the villa to pack and let Madam Peritakis know that she was leaving. She had no doubt that if Jason was there he would stay out of her way. He'd made it pretty clear that he didn't want any further confrontations with her.

She crept into the house and up to her room where she hurriedly threw her clothes into the two suitcases she'd brought with her from Canada. Shoving a few toilet articles and a change of underwear into an overnight bag, she put on jeans and shirt and went in search of Madam Peritakis. She found her in the little garden-room watering plants. She was wearing a house-coat. Her face was lined with fatigue and her eyelids were puffy and reddened. Lorna guessed she had been crying.

'Ah! My dear! I was worried about you,' she said, putting down her watering-can. 'You were not at breakfast and then the servants told me you had not been home.' She looked at Lorna searchingly. 'Is something wrong?'

'Yes. I ... I have to go ... back to Canada.' She lowered her eyes.

'Your family! Something has happened?' Jason's mother asked sharply.

Lorna found that she could not produce the excuse that there was 'trouble at home'. She was a bad liar at the best of times, and besides Madam Peritakis had been so kind to her, she deserved better. But she couldn't tell her the real reason either, so she said, 'My family's fine ... but ...' Her voice broke. 'I ... I can't stay here. Please accept that and don't ask me to explain.'

'It will be very lonely when you are gone.' The older woman looked bereft, and Lorna knew she was reeling from one piece of unpleasant news after another.

'I know about Nikos,' Lorna said, 'I'm so sorry.'

'It is a terrible grief to us,' she spoke slowly. 'Our name is disgraced.' Her eyes held Lorna's. 'Is it because of this that you wish to leave us?'

'Because of Nikos? Of course not! It makes no difference to the way I feel about you or . . .' she choked, 'or . . . any of you. How could it?'

'Oh! It might to some,' said Madam Peritakis, 'but I did not think it would to you.' She seated herself on a cane sofa. 'Come and sit with me, Lorna.' And when Lorna had perched herself beside her, she said, 'Will you be coming back?'

'No. I . . . I can't come back.' Her voice grew shaky again. 'I've given in my notice . . . I'm flying home at once.'

'I had hoped that you were beginning to think of this as your home,' Jason's mother said gently.

'I did . . . I do . . .' Lorna muttered and then gave up because the treacherous tears had flooded her eyes and she didn't trust herself to speak any more.

Madam Peritakis put her arm around the girl's slender shoulders. 'There, there child!' she comforted. 'It will be all right.'

'You've been so kind . . . I'll never forget you.' She tried to smile through a mist of tears.

Madam Peritakis said suddenly, 'Lorna I wish you to do something for me.'

'Of course.' Lorna found a tissue in the pocket of her jeans and wiped her eyes.

'I wish you to take a walk up the mountain.'

Lorna opened her tear-stained eyes wide. 'You want me to take a *walk*?' she echoed. '*Now!*'

'Yes . . . Up the mountain . . . I want you to go as far as the plateau. There is a small waterfall. It is about an hour's walk . . .'

'But I'm all packed and . . .'

'I want you to . . . to . . . to take a photograph of it for me,' Madam Peritakis went on in a sudden rush. 'I have been meaning to ask you to do this thing for some time. But . . . since you are leaving us so soon . . . there will be no other opportunity.' She bit her lips hesitantly, like an actress who has just delivered a bad reading.

'Of course I will, Madam,' Lorna answered. She was not too happy about this unexpected commission. A walk in the mountains . . . Jason's mountains . . . was the last thing she wanted to do. But she was under an obligation. It would have been ungracious to refuse. 'I'll go now,' she said, 'the light should be just right in about an hour.'

'Have you ever been up there?' Madam Peritakis asked.

'No, I haven't.' She had always followed the swift glassy curve of the stream down into the valley.

'It is one of my favourite places in the world. Up where the gods dwell.'

'Where the gods dwell?'

'It is said that the gods live high up in the mountains.' She patted Lorna's hand. 'When you get there ask them to be kind to you. Who knows—they may be listening.' She rose to her feet. 'And now you had better go, or . . . or you will miss the light,' she finished dismissively.

Within minutes Lorna was climbing the path Madam Peritakis had pointed out. But this exploration held no delights for her. She hardly noticed the sweet smell of thyme, and the stony fields of yellow flowers waving in the sunshine. The chattering of the shallow river seemed to be saying . . . *goodbye* . . . *goodbye* . . . So that Lorna—who hated all goodbyes—was overwhelmed with sadness.

She plodded on for some time, her legs like lead. Then the track, which had wound steadily upwards for about a mile, twisted round an outcrop of jagged rock.

She clambered around this barrier and was suddenly on the plateau.

Even in her numbed misery the beauty of the place made her gasp. It was bigger than she had imagined. A wide field protected on all sides by the mountain and backed by a smooth wall of rock that soared up into the clouds. The stream tumbled down over this escarpment in a steep waterfall. It was dwindled now by the summer's heat, but she could imagine the rushing torrents of springtime. There was a clear pool of sweet water at the base, rimmed with silvery sand. Some black-green cypresses grew around this oasis, and the air smelt of resin. Far away she could hear the muffled din of goat bells.

She stood for a long time in this heavenly spot whose beauty pierced her heart, then she unslung her camera and went to work.

When she had finished she removed her battered sun-hat and crouched by the pool to splash her hot face, then cupping her hands she drank from the falls. The ice-cold water tasted sharply of minerals within the rock.

Refreshed she stood up and tilted her head back to look at the savage peaks above. The idea of the gods living up here didn't seem so fantastic when you were surrounded by this awesome scenery, and she said aloud,

'Dear Greek gods, please make Jason love me again. Please make him love me.' She knew she was being childish, but she would have tried anything to win him back. Voodoo . . . black magic . . . the lot!

She bent to pick up her hat and stood dusting sand from the brim. Then she gave a little sudden cry and dropped it. For, like an answer to her prayer, he was standing by the outcrop of rock where the path joined the plateau.

'The gods cannot help you, Lorna,' he said quietly, and she wondered how he could be so cruel.

'I know that.' Her voice was quivering with shock. 'I know that you hate me. I didn't know you were there, or . . .'

'The gods cannot help you because I have never stopped loving you.' He took a step towards her. '*Hate* you! My darling . . .oh! my darling, I love you with all my heart.'

'It didn't sound like it when you sent me away.' She still flinched at the memory.

'That was because you had walked into a *trap*. A trap set for Nikos . . . When you came up that street I nearly *died*.' He came and stood before her and she was shocked at the lines of strain on his handsome face.

'Why didn't you tell me it was a trap? I thought you never wanted to see me again,' she choked, her eyes swimming with tears.

'Lorna! *Agapi mou*, don't cry.' He made to take her into his arms, but she avoided him. She had to have a fuller explanation before she surrendered.

He ran his hand through his sleek black hair so that it fell untidily over his brow. 'That little street was alive with police,' he said, 'they were hidden in every shop in the vicinity.'

She gazed at him steadily, her eyes still brimming. 'But why *there*?'

'I was waiting in a place where stolen goods can be sold,' he explained. 'We had reason to believe Nikos would try to dispose of the terracotta there. But when *you* arrived . . . *mou Theos*!' His face grew haggard at the memory. 'I was terrified that the police would think you were in partnership with Nikos. I was desperate to get you out of danger.'

'But why didn't you tell me of this trap beforehand?' Lorna said. 'Didn't you trust me to keep a secret?'

'I would trust you with my life, Lorna,' his eyes were a steady flame, 'but I had promised the inspector I would not tell anyone. We were acting on a . . . how is it? On a ... *hunch* only. My mother knew of our suspicions, but even she knew nothing of our plans.'

Lorna's first reaction was to protest that by not taking her into his confidence he was shutting her out of his life again, but she had learnt her bitter lesson, and instead she kept silent and waited for him to go on with his story.

'A little while after you had gone, as I had dreaded, Nikos arrived. He went into the shop and attempted to sell the little head, and we caught him red-handed as you say.' His face clouded. 'I did not enjoy that moment. Nikos broke down completely when he saw me. He confessed to stealing and selling the seal stones in the same way ... indeed the shop owner produced them in an attempt to lessen the charges against himself.' He sighed deeply. 'I suspected Nikos from the first,' he said. 'I wish to God I had been mistaken.'

'Where is Nikos now?' Lorna asked.

'After he had been taken to the police station ... *mou Theos*! That was dreadful Lorna. He cried like a woman and begged me to save him ... and I was powerless.' His mouth tensed, and she could sense the pain in him. 'I contacted my mother at her meeting and got her to come to Rethimnon with our lawyer. I paid bail and then, after much discussion long into the night, Nikos agreed to await trial at the monastery near our village. Perhaps the good brothers will be able to help him to find courage.'

He took her unresisting hand in his and at his touch she gave a sob and burst into tears. With a cry he gathered her into his arms, stroking her hair, murmuring brokenly in his own tongue, kissing away her tears that now fell unchecked.

'*Agapi mou* it is all right ... do not cry ... it is all right now.'

'I've ... I've been so unhappy ...' she gulped.

'I, too, my darling.' He smoothed a strand of hair away from her wet cheek. 'I am nothing without you, Lorna,' he said, 'last night, when we returned home and

I could not find you ...' He held her tighter and she put her arms round his waist and clung to him. 'Where did you run to?'

'I stayed with Maria.' She snuggled closer. 'I couldn't stay at the villa. Not after you'd told me to go away.'

'I did not mean from me,' he groaned, and she kissed his warm cheek.

'I know that now,' she whispered.

He pulled her down to sit next to him on the warm sand. 'Thank God I found you here,' he said. 'I was nearly mad with despair.'

'How did you know where to look?' She remembered her impassioned plea and giggled, glancing over his head to the high mountain tops. 'The gods must have been listening after all.'

'They had a little help from my mother,' he smiled.

'Your mother?'

'She knew I had gone again to find news of you and she phoned the taverna to say I would find you here at the plateau.'

'She wanted a photograph ... she said.' Lorna chuckled, remembering that sudden brusque request.

'She knows how much I love you *kookla mou*,' he said.

'And she doesn't mind?'

'*Mind!* Why should she? You must have sensed that she is very fond of you.'

'But I'm not Greek ... I mean ... I'm afraid I might not fit into your world ...'

He suddenly looked grave. 'Have I ever told you that you do not fit into my world?'

'No ... only ...'

'The only person who ever mentions it is you, Lorna,' he pointed out. 'Perhaps *you* do not want to fit into it?'

'I do! I love Crete. I love your world, Jason.' She clasped her hands as if in prayer. 'When I bumped into you like that in Rethimnon I wanted to tell you how sorry I was that I've been so ... so difficult. To explain that I get terrified sometimes because . . . Oh! I don't know . . . I'm afraid I won't fit in . . . that you'll turn away from me. It makes me behave like a fool.'

He took her hands in his and gently unlaced her fingers. 'I thought it was something like that,' he said. 'The best way to belong to this country is to marry into it.' She stared into his cat's eyes. 'Will you marry me, Lorna? Say you will. I love you so much. I want to have children with you . . . grow old with you.'

'Oh Jason! I . . .' she hesitated, recalling the Cretan insistence on virginal brides.

'You must not think I wish you to give up your career, my darling.' He gripped her hands hard. 'When the work on the dig is completed you could do your book. I could help you, perhaps. We could travel through Greece together.'

He was pleading with her—her beautiful proud Jason—pleading.

'If we married I couldn't carry a bouquet of flowers from the Chaste Tree,' she said.

He looked nonplussed. 'The Chaste Tree?'

'Like Ariadne did. I'm not a virgin.' She prayed she wouldn't lose him, but she had to be honest with him.

'But you are not a child like Ariadne. You are a woman. Also it is clear that you are not promiscuous.' He asked her softly, 'How many lovers have you had Lorna?'

'One,' she confessed. 'The man I once thought I was going to marry.'

'I believe that I can wipe him from your memory,' he said, and she smiled because he'd done that from the beginning. 'I do not want you changed, Lorna. But I *do* want to bind you to me forever.' He looked at her with such hungry love that she was filled with a wild happiness.

'Yes Jason,' she answered him. 'Of course I'll marry you.'

'Soon?' he insisted. 'You will marry me soon?'

'As soon as you like. I don't want to wait a moment longer than we have to.'

'*Agapi mou!*' He kissed her possessively and they fell back on the sand, his lips still claiming hers. A throb of desire flowed from her throat down to the hidden, secret part of her.

When the kiss ended he held her close, stroking her spine with firm strong fingers. 'When we get back I will phone your brother,' he whispered softly, his mouth against her ear. 'We can be married either in Canada, or here in the village.'

She remembered her dream of walking beside her brother to the little church, where Jason would be waiting for her to start their life together. 'I'd like to be married here,' she told him.

'*Poli kala!* I shall bring out your family for the wedding.' He started to gently kiss her throat, and she turned and thrust herself against him, for every part of her was longing for his touch.

His lips found her mouth again, but this time his kiss was almost brutal in its passion, and she responded ardently, matching his passion with her own, until they were like two flames in the spinning golden air.

Much later, when the shadows had lengthened, she stretched languorously and looked up at the limitless sky. The sand felt like silk against her warm skin.

He leaned over her and tenderly kissed her naked breasts. 'My beautiful woman . . . mine,' he murmured, his voice husky with fulfilment.

She laughed softly and turned on her side. 'You know what?' she said, tracing the dark hair on his chest with her finger.

'What my love?'

'I haven't eaten properly for days . . . I'm starving!' she grinned.

'And it is getting late. We must go back.' He caught her stroking finger and kissed it. 'But we will never get back if you continue to do that,' he warned, and she smiled at him mischievously.

When they had dressed and were ready to leave they stood for a moment at the outcrop of rock, looking back at the little waterfall and the beach of silvery sand.

'I will build our house here,' Jason said. 'Our married home. Would you like that?'

She looked at him, her eyes as clear as the glinting water of the stream. There was not a single doubt in her mind.

'Our home,' she said, tasting the words like wine. 'Home . . . home at last.'

Hello!

You've come to the end of this story and we truly hope that you enjoyed it.

If you did (or even if you didn't!), have you ever thought that you might like to try writing a romance yourself?

You may not know it, but Mills & Boon are always looking for good new authors and we read every manuscript sent to us. Although we are proud to say that our standards are high and we can't promise every aspiring author success, unless you try you'll never know whether one of those new authors could be you!

Who knows, from being a reader you might become one of our well-loved authors, giving pleasure to thousands of readers around the world. In fact, many of our authors were originally keen Mills & Boon readers who thought, "I can do that" — and they did! So if you've got the love story of the century bubbling away inside your head, don't be shy: write to us for details today, sending a stamped addressed envelope. We'd really like to hear from you!

The Editors

Please write to:

Editorial Dept
Mills & Boon Ltd
15-16 Brook's Mews
London W1A 1DR

The Puppet Master
PIPPA CLARKE
The Iron Heart
EDWINA SHORE
Pacific Disturbance
VANESSA GRANT
Once More with Feeling
NATALIE SPARK
Four brand new titles, from four brand new authors.
All in one attractive gift pack for just £4.40, published on 9th August.
Fall in love with Mills & Boon's new authors.

The Rose of Romance

Mills & Boon

Take 4 Exciting Books Absolutely FREE

Love, romance, intrigue... all are captured for you by Mills & Boon's top-selling authors. By becoming a regular reader of Mills & Boon's Romances you can enjoy 6 superb new titles every month plus a whole range of special benefits: your very own personal membership card, a free monthly newsletter packed with recipes, competitions, exclusive book offers and a monthly guide to the stars, plus extra bargain offers and big cash savings.

AND an Introductory FREE GIFT for YOU.
Turn over the page for details.

As a special introduction we will send you four exciting Mills & Boon Romances Free and without obligation when you complete and return this coupon.

At the same time we will reserve a subscription to Mills & Boon Reader Service for you. Every month, you will receive 6 of the very latest novels by leading Romantic Fiction authors, delivered direct to your door. You don't pay extra for delivery — postage and packing is always completely Free. There is no obligation or commitment — you can cancel your subscription at any time.

You have nothing to lose and a whole world of romance to gain.

Just fill in and post the coupon today to MILLS & BOON READER SERVICE, FREEPOST, P.O. BOX 236, CROYDON, SURREY CR9 9EL.

Please Note:- READERS IN SOUTH AFRICA write to Mills & Boon, Postbag X3010, Randburg 2125, S. Africa.

FREE BOOKS CERTIFICATE

To: Mills & Boon Reader Service, FREEPOST, P.O. Box 236, Croydon, Surrey CR9 9EL.

Please send me, free and without obligation, four Mills & Boon Romances, and reserve a Reader Service Subscription for me. If I decide to subscribe I shall, from the beginning of the month following my free parcel of books, receive six new books each month for £6 60, post and packing free. If I decide not to subscribe, I shall write to you within 10 days. The free books are mine to keep in any case. I understand that I may cancel my subscription at any time simply by writing to you. I am over 18 years of age.

Please write in BLOCK CAPITALS.

Signature _____

Name _____

Address _____

_____ Post code _____

SEND NO MONEY — TAKE NO RISKS.

Please don't forget to include your Postcode.

Remember, postcodes speed delivery. Offer applies in UK only and is not valid to present subscribers. Mills & Boon reserve the right to exercise discretion in granting membership. If price changes are necessary you will be notified.

6R   Offer expires 31st December 1985

EP86